I AM
Stories

I AM
Stories

Up at the Retreat

Fran Shaw

Indications Press
New York

www.franshawbooks.com

With heartfelt thanks to all who shared their stories.

Design: Yuko Uchikawa, Erin Hollaway Palmer
Cover Concept: David Shaw
Editorial Guidance: Lillian Firestone, Sue Kagan,
Aubrey Paull

ISBN (paperback): 978-0-9639100-5-9
ISBN (e-book): 978-0-9639100-6-6

Library of Congress Control Number: 2021943635

For RDS, ever present.

～

"Then comes a moment of feeling
the wings you've grown, lifting."
—Rumi

CONTENTS

*There are two men in me. There is the one
who when he is centered, when he is in relation
with higher energies, is intense, alive, generous.
And then, at another moment, back in my
usual state, the one who thinks he is in charge,
controlling everything—fears this, wishes that,
all my problems. Can let him go for a moment.*

*There is a subtle energy penetrating the body,
a higher Intelligence that I can recognize because
I'm a human being. With a very active attention,
I can receive this energy. When this energy is
there and I am aware of it moment by moment,
I begin to be. All my thoughts, feelings, ideas are
nothing compared to this precious treasure,
this quality of energy that is not mine but what
I am. The living mystery. . . I AM.*

—LeClair

Before Abraham was, I AM.

—John 8:58

*Oh, do not ask, "What is it?"
Let us go and make our visit.*

—T. S. Eliot

Up at the Retreat

Higher consciousness at 6000 feet.

This is the first, wildest, and wisest
thing I know, that the soul exists, and that
it is built entirely out of attention.

—Mary Oliver

In the transcendent light of the Elysian Fields coffee shop, in the lofty atmosphere of the Matterhorn mini-mart, a group of Americans talk of conscious living and convenient shopping. On a summer's day, we're traveling through the Swiss Alps on our way to a weeklong retreat at a place nicknamed, by the neighbors, Le Zoo. The compound includes a large chalet, a small chalet, and a meditation/dining hall. Spectacular alpine vistas surround the property, along with sloping meadows, dirt roads carved out of the mountainside, and the prying eyes of the locals who think the chalet is being used as a sanatorium. Actually, something else is going on there. Something amazing.

The journey that brings us here began years ago when each of us met a particular spiritual practice for awakening. Now we come for a period of intensive "inner work" with a rare guide and eighty invitees from around the world—France, Switzerland, Canada, Britain, Holland, Armenia, Mexico, Israel, South America. All of us hear the call of the higher. Yet who among us, despite baggage and type, crosses the threshold to awaken? At any instant is there enough attention to join with the vital force of life?

Each of us hopes for a taste of real transformation when an unknown dimension suddenly opens. Each wants to live a fully human life, in balance, aware and appreciative of all aspects of our nature, including the apparent self of body-mind-feeling and the hidden Self of un-nameable (call it) life-force energy. Its blazing up brings a new state. As our guide LeClair puts it, "All these forces in me that usually have their way in my ordinary state because there is no higher force there—now all are drawn up in the current. Ego, features, are still there, but now they serve. And when they serve the higher force, all is changed. With attending to presence, allowing higher forces to enter, staying collected, returning, we can live in a new way."

Who is LeClair? A widower in his seventies, highly educated, French-speaking, heir to a specific spiritual transmission, and quite simply, a man whose wakefulness is contagious. Understanding appears in us through mutual alignment in a flow. If these pages give the impression that every time he speaks he "teaches," that is not at all the case; a more accurate description would be to say that the way he moves through life is the teaching. On the mountain many of us experience for the first time the difference between something we "do" and Something we *receive*. "If it is 'my' attention, that runs up the mountain, sees obstacles, does this or that, it is not this other Attention, which *transforms*." What he models for us is a heightened sensitivity to a finer energy—higher Intelligence, "this sacred Attention"—the teacher in you, the teacher in me. "And even subtler energies can come into you. The Light can come into you." Beyond that, all is a mystery.

It's a bumpy week. The tug of beliefs, self-talk, self-image. It is striking, though, when after a few days the usual observations ("i should, i can't, i don't") give way to "higher seeing," (as LeClair describes) "when it does not matter what is seen; you are more awake in this finer energy." In moments of total receptivity there appears direct contact with a luminous dimension, pure Consciousness perhaps, and the possibility of being a conduit for it to come into the world—for me, for you, for the earth and more. Until the next bump.

We meet daily in small groups with LeClair, take on mindful tasks around the property, and come together at meals. Each day brings moments of a relation with—no words for it—an intensely alive vibration; we learn to pay attention to That. At the time of these events, over two decades ago, it was not clear the struggles that many of us were going through on the mountain until described to me during phone interviews. A few of our questions in those days: What helps "mobilize attention"? What makes possible "receiving, transforming, and embodying energies consciously"? Collecting people's accounts then and writing about them now has been eye-opening. I AM *Not Stories*. Nevertheless, a short-story cycle emerged in which a blending occurs—their experience, my experience; then, now.

But is it ever the Whole story?

Because in these pages we find seekers we know but in our *younger* years. Much is different today. Names have been changed for privacy's sake, and the narrator-at-play is given license to grease the wheels with a touch of humor. In hindsight, my younger self depicted here (attractively redefined, of course) seems dedicated but "unskillful," identified with my-this-my-that and ready to unpack for you (as now?) the contents of this very special hamper that is me. Clean me up to wake up? *Before the ecstasy, the laundry?*

At the retreat it's more like, *During the laundry, the ecstasy.*

But sometimes it feels like, *After the ecstasy, the inadequacy.*

Bless-ed let-down! When feeling the "lack" becomes the call. When the body fills with attention, and heightened sound and light flood in. When an indescribable energy arises to be recognized every second—

merged with—so it can continue to appear. When the "lack" and the *shoulds* vaporize like stuff in a dream. So what is real? What never ceases to be? Is there Something here that is not suffering at all?

i don't know but sometimes I AM.

That alone seems miraculous, given what we're faced with. Even as we are we rise.

It surely feels that way on the mountain when suddenly, by grace, we are vibrating higher together, different creatures for the moment. The Presence has us again. Lights us up. Lets us laugh at ourselves. Brings joy. Opens a tenderness that wishes others well. A wondrous relief! We are free. We are grateful. We are One. We awaken. And so it begins.

~

DAILY SCHEDULE

6:30 a.m.	Guided Meditation
8:00	Breakfast; Inner Task Posed
9:30	Team Projects; Individual Meetings with LeClair

Cleaning, dishwashing, preparing food, gardening, building, repairing, painting, decorating, sewing, doing laundry, translating, rehearsing, and more.

11:30	Coffee Break
Noon	Team Projects and Meetings Continue
1:30	Lunch; Stories, Questions, Discussion
2:30	Rest
3:30	Team Projects Continue
5:00	Sacred-Dance Classes; Small-Group Meetings with LeClair
8:00	Dinner; Stories
9:30	Evening Presentation, Music, Readings
SATURDAY	Sauna; Final-Evening Celebration
SUNDAY	Breakfast; Departure

Alice's Bookshelf

*Alice questions
her judgment.*

Something is supposed to happen, but something else happens. Isn't that the way it always goes? I'm with Alice and three men driving through Switzerland. For the tenth time, she looks at her watch. Her plan is to arrive early at the retreat and get a good bed. Now we're stuck in a slow car winding its way along narrow switchbacks taking us higher into the Alps. As we approach a town busy with a summer street fair, traffic stops.

One of the men asks, "Shall we get out?"

Keep going, Alice wants to say—but of course the men will stop for coffee. The town is lovely, yes, cocoa-colored chalets with window boxes cascading red geraniums; booth-lined streets filled with people buying laceworks, cheeses, and giant chocolate bars wrapped in alpine scenes. But it's distracting.

How can she arrive in a collected state with all of this going on? Jittery as a flea.

Next to the parking lot is a small church. No one inside. Alice sits down in a pew. A relief, just to listen to the quiet. Sunlight streams through the yellows and blues and greens of a stained-glass window. The retreat has begun.

Back on the street at a café, she joins us New Yorkers, all from the same Center where we go for spiritual fare on the Upper East Side. It was at that venue that Alice first heard LeClair when he visited the States. Rather wonderful what he said (although she can't recall a word of it), and it was enough to make her cross an ocean for this chance, by invitation, to work with him for a week. But now the whole event makes her inexplicably nervous.

Tom from the Center announces to everyone, "We were told not to go up to the chalet before five."

Alice looks away. A lump forms in the pit of her stomach. No chance now to get the bed.

"I've seen you before." Tom pulls up a

chair next to her. Introductions. "Where you from?"

"New York." (Connecticut.)

"Have you worked with LeClair before?"

"First time." She surveys her fingernails as if they are damaged goods marked down twice. She doesn't want to talk. She wants to get going.

"Nervous? No need." He smiles a sticky, intimate smile. "I like your watch."

Rose gold. "Thanks." She shakes her youthful mane of dark hair away from her face, framing perfect grey eyes that are just a touch prominent.

Tom sails words over her head. "Working on a book…. Cars backed up all the way to Montauk…. Mother had an exhibit…. That actor who's sleeping with… Broadway show…. Maybe we could see one sometime?"

Croissants and butter arrive. Tom unfastens the bottom button on his vest. "Love this French *beurre*," he says, reaching for it.

She looks at him as if he has *merde* on his lips.

Hours later, our car drives back and forth through the highest village on the mountain. Unmarked roads. No address. Sketchy directions. No one there has heard of the place. It's a rite of passage just to find it. Almost five o'clock. The driver parks in town; he asks at a local shop, then points to a steep path between two buildings. We descend on foot. But which chalet?

"Where the hell is it!" shouts one of the men. Laughter shatters the stillness.

Alice panics. *No! LeClair will hear about how loud we are—ugly Americans—*

"There. Down there." One of the men recognizes the twin-peaked rooftops of the chalet, with its grassy terrace bounded by a low wall where the land drops off to a meadow dotted with flowers.

Alice wheels her bag on the dusty lane as the sun beats down. A heap of luggage by the roadside. She parks hers near the pile and walks toward a group of men and women. Arrivals or departures?

Suddenly, a whirring—

Her silver Tumi rolling down the slope! She catches it at the edge of a steep drop, but it pulls her down. Now she is flat on the ground, dirty, with a scraped knee. She pours water on it from her Evian bottle. Is the Tumi dented? She drags the leaden thing back up the path.

At the chalet, bags clutter the walkway. Two men stop smoking to watch her rumpled bleeding form come down the path. Not at all how she wanted to arrive! Heart beating fast, Alice stands with others waiting to hear room assignments. Women bound up the stairs. Only a few bags left. The final name is read.

Her name is not on the list.

Her face is as white as a Porthault sheet. Will she be allowed to stay? "Excuse me," Alice approaches the woman with the list. "My name wasn't read."

Paulina, LeClair's assistant, lowers her clipboard. "There's a second list. They're making it up now."

An hour later, Alice enters the chalet, up the stairs, one flight, two flights, barely consoled by the possibility of a view. At last, the North Dormitory: bunk beds that mock comfort; vases of dead flowers arranged in lifelike groupings; a small white table providing the only real color in the room. Yet this is not her final destination, for every bed is already claimed.

A ladder takes her up to a slant-ceilinged loft with six "mattresses" on the floor, all with gear except one. A damp, woodsy odor. Knotty pine everywhere makes her long for some sheetrock—or her bedroom at home: the pink walls; the paintings of ballerinas; the ruffled canopy over the bed; the grandfather clock, representing a long line of genteel anal retentivity. She struggles to lift her giant bag through the opening. Her "bed" is a slim foam pad, no wider than her yoga mat, directly under the slant-y part of the roof and inches from the opening for the ladder. Claustrophobic, indeed. Surely she will hit her head every time she gets out of bed. Will she be able to sleep like this, in a space two-feet wide, at risk of rolling over and falling down the hole?

Inside the meditation hall we all sit on cushions on the floor in rows facing front. Too tired to keep her back upright, Alice chooses one of the chairs along the rear wall, by the exit.

LeClair comes in. He glances at her. His

oval face, dominated by the eyes; the broad forehead; the touch of grey in front of the ears. He walks to the front and surveys the room. "So glad to see so many of my friends." He asks who takes coffee in the morning; hands go up; someone counts them.

"We suffer together for a few days"—here he grins—"and then you can stand anything." The little joke, and his voice—the way it makes her listen—"Think why you have come."

Alice sits up straight. The longer she listens, the lighter she feels. Turning thoughts drop away. There is nowhere else on earth she wishes to be.

This new state opens again the next morning as she sits on the terrace gliding an iron across a cloth napkin, glad for the pile. Surely it must be an inner sun coming out because Alice never irons. Back in the States, it's a life going on in her head, thinking, worrying, judging—the usual self-torture. Teaching yoga brings relief but not freedom. The thousand books in her library offer little help. "I don't want to spend my life at the mercy of everything that happens. I want to wake up," she said before leaving, to her mother, who herself has yet to find the magic behind the bright hard glitter.

Yet here, in this unknown energy arising.... Is consciousness contagious? Clouds billow up as grand as the peaks. Now all she wants is to get invited back next summer. In the meadow, each time a cow moves one step, the valley rings with cowbells.

Tom comes by. "Can you hold my place in line for a few minutes?" He's been sitting on "the Bench" outside the smaller chalet where people wait to speak with LeClair.

"Sure." Her friendliness surprises her. There under the eaves she recognizes the argumentative woman from breakfast.

"Have you been in to see him yet?" the woman asks. Her fingernails are turkey red.

"I'm not waiting to see him. I'm just holding a place for a friend."

"Really? I've been preparing for this all year."

A man arrives, sees the line, and goes away. Another comes down the steps and walks right in. Summoned? So many people, so needy—Alice vows she won't be one of them.

Tom returns. "Thanks, Alice." Later, he comes around the corner. "I was in there for half an hour."

A breeze stirs the tips of the tall grasses. *Am I missing out?*

Just as she irons the last of the napkins, LeClair walks past. Introduce herself? Speak to him in her high-school French? She hadn't bargained for the retreat being mostly in French. *No matter. It's not about content; it's about connection.*

At lunch, LeClair confirms, "There is an energy I can be related to. As human beings, we have the capacity for another dimension to appear simultaneously with all this that thinks, feels, reacts. Related to this influence, for us, a new world opens."

The meal ends with a reading from an anthology for sale. A particular line piques Alice's interest: *"The only discovery is this energy."* She buys the book and—great idea—will ask LeClair to sign it.

A day later at the outdoor buffet, she sits on a folding chair near him. Her chance. She runs up the stairs to the dorm and gets the book.

"Who is this lady?" says LeClair, seated, looking up at her.

She squats down, says her name, and hands him the book. "Will you sign this for me?"

He takes it and sets it aside. They speak briefly. She's not sure if he understands her English. But she finally spoke to him!

It makes her happy every time she thinks of their moment together. But days go by— no book. *He's busy. A little thing. He has forgotten. Let it go.*

In the dining hall, Alice checks the place settings for dinner. She likes spotting where something is missing—a spoon here, a glass there—and providing what is needed. When she finishes, she goes to the Bench, having bought a second copy of the book.

Across the valley, the last rays of sun make the peaks shine. And she shines, too. If he would come out now, she'd thank him for the week—and he'd see in her eyes just how fine a week it is!

But twice LeClair comes and goes through the doorway, not looking her way.

Finally, Alice intercepts him with the

book. "Could you—"

He says kindly, "You press me."

No! She apologizes and walks quickly to her dorm. *Ruined everything! A nuisance. A show-off.* Now she'll never get invited back—and her entire well-being depends on returning. She resolves never to bother him again.

The following day when it comes time for her favorite activity, the sacred dances, she considers taking a shower instead. It's the last class, though, so she attends.

Thirty people line up in five rows, six across. Alice goes to the back.

Paulina, the instructor, walks up to her. "Don't you want to take your usual place?"

Alice is obliged to go to the front row.

The piano plays. Paulina shows the movements. Now there is no room for a single thought. It takes every bit of attention to foresee the next posture, keep the count, move in time, in the right sequence, with the others. When class is over, Alice stands in place with everyone. The room is still. The same in her.

"Now, to move intentionally, from one's own initiative," says Paulina, and the hall empties.

Alice thanks Paulina. "Such a good class. I wish I could be in this state all the time."

"Why don't you try?" comes the reply.

Alice learns that LeClair is off-site until dinner. No one on the Bench. She sits. Sensitive ears in the silence. A hidden stream, that she hears but cannot see, rushes down in freshets from the high ground. Piano music starts, from the dining hall. And then: singing. The choral group rehearsing "Adoramus." Voices rise up in harmony. To her it is the sound of human life fulfilled.

Paulina comes out of the chalet. "His English isn't so good," she says as she hands Alice the book. "He had someone help him. He spent fifteen minutes on it."

There's a handwritten inscription on the title page. He didn't forget. It was no small thing to him. He needed time to compose something in English—for her. And what he wrote—such good news! As if they are long-time companions on a path.

"He's a precious resource. We want to conserve him," Paulina says, sitting down. "The first year I came here I needed to ask him something. I waited on this bench for an hour, looking at the mountains. The whole place was illuminated. I felt transformed. I got up and left."

"Why?"

"I realized my question got answered. Or that I didn't have one—no ego there anymore with a question. Sometimes on this bench you find a bit of enlightenment."

Alice describes all this to me on the phone, once she is back home. Her mother has taken to calling her Mary Sunshine. In the afterglow, Alice is determined to go again next summer, now that she knows the fish is in the pond. What she values most is what comes to life in her on the mountain, side by side with LeClair and others who wish to awaken.

The following July, Alice arrives early at the chalet and is told to take any bed in the North Dormitory. She runs up the stairs. Last year, she eyed the semi-private alcove with only two beds. *Empty!* She happily puts a bag on each, saving the other place for me. Next to her bed runs a very long shelf—the only space like it in the dorm—on which she places lotions, potions, photos, a covey of Limoges quail, and the complete works of Rumi, making the space cozy at once. Because what if things become uncomfortable? Here will be a little bit of home where she can get away.

Soon the dorm is full of activity.

"Everyone can be a channel for higher energies."

"I like the Discovery channel."

"Very few people know about this place. It's a jealously guarded secret."

"You can come here and still not know about it."

She recognizes women from last summer. She reads them like her beloved books. *Jane Ire. Hedda Gabber. June the Obscure.* This one talks too much; that one complains; this one analyzes, all about yesterday; that one is fearful, all about tomorrow; this one uses her suffering to manipulate others; that one needs recognition of spiritual status; this one believes in the one who thinks she knows. *Like me.*

Alice. The sharpest knife in the drawer. Self-aware, and stuck in clueless.

Clipboard in hand, Paulina asks for Alice. They go into the hall. "LeClair wants you to sleep there." Paulina points to a bunk behind drapery in the stairwell. "When you pull the curtain, it's private. He thought you might like that. There's even a little window above the bed."

Give up her alcove? She knows from last year who sleeps in the stairwell above: the worst snorer exiled from the men's tent. "I really want to stay in the dorm with the others," says Alice. But has anyone ever not done what LeClair asked?

Day 2. At breakfast in the dining hall as LeClair listens, people describe their experiences. Alice is losing herself in their stories when she hears that *taking in impressions without judgment is about being related to higher energy.* Really? As she climbs the stairs to her dorm, she's thinking, Is that even possible—

Male voices in French. A handsome Scandinavian wearing a tool-belt stands by her bed.

"This is the women's dorm," she reminds him.

He takes the measuring tape from his belt and leans over her mattress, nearly stepping on her pillow—

Alice shrieks. "What are you doing!"

"We're building bookshelves."

"We don't need them. There's no room for them." Cordial as a crocodile.

The men leave and do not return.

That night in the dining hall, she spots Nordic ski god and sits down next to him. "How was your day?" She looks as if she's going to leap into his mouth.

Day 3. The men again, in her alcove. This time LeClair is with them. Seeing him, she turns to leave—but hearing his instructions, she blurts, "We don't want bookshelves. It's dangerous to sleep with books over your head."

LeClair appears not to have heard. He says a few final words to the men. On his way out, he glances at Alice's shelf-full of personal items.

Horrors!

She looks like a caged woodchuck. *Exposed! Selfish. Comfort hound. And now he knows.* Alice in Blunderland. *Why did I open my mouth?*

In bed at night she cries softly. Things have to be a certain way and now they're not. The chance for something, lost. Such a strain, holding up a front, protecting... what? A bubble, a mirage—*self-image*, she realizes, there amid her traitorous possessions.

Day 4. At the early morning sitting, tears. She needs to wipe her drippy nose but doesn't move. Shifting focus helps for a few minutes, but at breakfast, she sits way in the back, slumped over her bowl of muesli.

Someone speaks about feeling *dépassé* (overwhelmed). "It's like a string is cut. I fall down."

"These ups and downs we go through when we're self-centered," LeClair says, "we are all like this, experiencing associations, frustrations. To let that be, but to feel some pure attention, even as you are, suffering, tired—a beautiful landscape. So remarkable when there is, along with that, a moment of attention—quite different. And the seeing, this contact with pure attention, is freeing."

And then Alice hears, "Life can be distressing, but the light of consciousness can be in me."

Yes, she thinks, life *is* distressing—*but the light of consciousness can be in me!*

Breakfast over, Alice gets up and turns toward the aisle.

LeClair comes down the aisle and not breaking stride looks directly at her. It is a long moment in which their eyes meet and Alice feels certain his words were for her. *He sees. He understands. Everything is okay!*

It's like the sun coming out. Grateful! And so glad to be here. Not only that. For the rest of the day—and week—people look different to her. No judgments in her at all. Someone speaks and all Alice sees is the light there behind the eyes. Someone is in distress and all Alice wants is to comfort. Even talking with me is different—we are vibrating differently.

"For the first time, other people's suffering is more important than my own," she says.

"I know. You can hardly believe it. One glance and you receive this amazing kind of acceptance," I say. "When you feel accepted, you can give."

"I can't change myself," says Alice, "but when this energy is here, it's a miracle.

The Goodness of it pours through me and changes everything."

Last Day. Departure time. Alice cannot leave until she thanks LeClair. At his door she hears voices speaking French. He is meeting with someone, and she will have to interrupt—

She knocks and walks in. LeClair turns to the other person and says of Alice, "*Cette femme est faite pour l'amour.*"

Alice does not translate the French then—something about love—because she is focused on not disturbing them. "I just came to say goodbye."

LeClair gets up. "Mother Alice," he teases.

"Yes, yes, I know."

He stands with her at the door. "You are luminous."

A sudden shower of roses!

Her feet barely touch the ground as she climbs the stairs to the dorm. *Cette femme…* This woman… is made for… love. Can it be?

Alice turns the corner to find the alcove exactly as it was that first day, a lifetime ago. There was no bookshelf built that week.

When Ego Left Town

*Can Nicholas and Tom
repair the past?*

"Uh-huh." Nicholas has nothing to say to Tom and dribbles it out by the syllable. It's the first time he's seen his old friend since their blowup a year ago. Now, coincidentally, both men have returned to Switzerland to the same spiritual retreat and are thrown together on the same project.

Nicholas has no idea Tom is there that first morning. LeClair, in charge, takes several of the men on a tour of the property to show them the week's tasks. A rock wall by the garden, a stone barbecue facing the Matterhorn. Standing by the storage shed, Nicholas hears about a workbench. An engineer, he likes building things—his inner world rejoices at the sight of a laminated beam—so he signs up. Later, when he goes inside the shed—

"Hi," says Tom. "How ya been?"

"Okay. You?"

"Busy." The place is empty but Tom fills it with himself. "Research… Columbia… shamanic plant studies… expanding aware-ness… kinds of attention… sensation of the body… life-force energy… healing… hemp."

Nicholas looks at him as if he's speaking in tongues. "So, Tom, what brings you here" *if your life is so perfect.*

The conversation lurches forward. Tom, the charmer, announces his intention to construct the best workbench ever, issuing instructions about how it's all to be done. He charms by erosion. But nothing is level in there—rocky ledge floor. He starts dig-ging at it with a chisel.

"Love what you're doing to the floor," says Nicholas.

"We've got to even it out so the bench will be level," says Tom, ever willing to work as long as it takes. "Don't they have a machine for this sort of thing?"

"Annnh," Nicholas makes a noise like creaking wood.

The next morning he walks into the shed

to find Tom demonstrating a complicated breathing exercise to two newcomers. As they leave, Tom tells them, "Come see me later. I'll be here after lunch. Bring your questions."

"Is it a good idea," says Nicholas, liver-yang rising, "instructing new people like that?" It's the same kind of careless, self-serving behavior that tanked their friendship. It still hurts.

Tom is ruffled. "I have no idea your point."

So dense. "Giving exercises and life advice. It's not our place to do that here. Why do you need LeClair? Sounds like you should be running the week."

"They're young. They're filled with beliefs," says Tom. "Beliefs interfere with direct perception. We're here to help each other, aren't we?"

Nicholas mumbles, "Not put our foot on other people's necks."

"You talk to me like I'm always wrong. I've been thinking—"

"There you go exaggerating again."

"Maybe your ideas are an obstacle to you now. It's all unknown, right? Does that make sense?"

Wants my validation. "I'm not here to make sense. I'm here to wake up."

"They asked me. I can bring change—"

"But not transformation."

Strangers trapped in an elevator. So disheartening, to be angry *here.* Nicholas suffers with that.

Compassionate listening? Loving speech? Passive. Aggressive. At night in bed rehearsing what he could say to give that smug ego a smack. *Yikes! Am I only that?*

During the lunch discussion with everyone, LeClair says, "For many years we try methods, but then, at moments, there is enough energy for a sensitivity to appear, and then for this Intelligence to appear. It's not the methods that produce it. It's letting everything be, inside, just as it is, and opening to the attention."

Speak up? Because it feels impossible to "let it be" when roiling inside. Better not say anything now, though, Nicholas decides. He'll hear himself talk and know when he's full of it. Besides, it's too hard to concentrate, being sleep-deprived after two nights in the dorm listening to Tom snore like a herd of congested llamas. (Never mind the looks the men give Tom at the sinks in the morning. Oblivious.)

Later in the basement Nicholas searches for an extension cord. LeClair is there, taking inventory. When asked how things are going, Nicholas reports, "No sleep. Tom snores so loud, it's driving us up the wall."

LeClair raises an eyebrow. "What is this 'driving up wall'?" French, not English, is his first language, and he collects American slang for future brandishing.

"It means becoming so irritated that you'd climb the walls to get away."

Within the hour, Nicholas finds Tom in the men's dorm, packing.

"Did you ask them to change where I sleep?" says Tom.

A nasty turn.

"We can't take the snoring."

Tom zips his duffel. "I'm getting my own space in the main chalet. Over the stairs. Pull the curtains and it's like a private room."

All afternoon Nicholas avoids the shed.

The next day at breakfast a question is posed: *Is it important to work with others for consciousness?* At lunch, after hearing people's observations, LeClair says, "Working with others. It is the opportunity to see myself. To see when I am related to an energy, and when perhaps there is a little tension around it. Even when there is a reaction, one can have a Look upon oneself, no matter what is taking place. If you prefer that Look, this other energy can appear, and you can become stable in this Attention. And the mark of that is that even for a short while you feel related to the world, everything and everyone."

Nicholas must contribute, say something, not having uttered a word all week and the retreat half gone. In the usual parlance of the discipline, he speaks of using a certain tool and "sensing my hand while—"

LeClair interrupts, "I don't want to hear about sensation."

Cut off. In front of everyone. Nicholas barely registers what comes next, his mind is going so fast: *If he doesn't want to hear that, what does he want to hear? He doesn't understand me. I don't communicate.*

After lunch, Nicholas lies down but cannot rest. He walks the property in the rain—but there are still so many people. Hidden from view, he sits in the stone alcove above the garden.

Across the valley, clouds having no choice in the matter snag on the peaks. *Obviously it isn't good enough,* what Nicholas said or how he said it, and that is humiliating. But how long will he have to feel this way?

The rain stops. Shafts of light come down through the clouds. Rays of sunlit air. The valley, flecked with gold. And it occurs to him, *Can I wake up now, even like this?*

If he had to put into words what happened then, he might say that *Something appeared in me that isn't hurt at all.*

He knocks on LeClair's door. The two men sit by the window. Now Nicholas can be sincere. "It takes a lot for me to be around Tom. We had a fight. I moved away. I haven't seen him since." Nicholas shakes his head. "We were friends for years. I've known him since Catholic school. I should have some compassion."

"Yes, I wish to have compassion—but it isn't me that can have compassion; it is this

Intelligence in me that can have compassion. I see my friend acting this way and that, but I observe, open, so this sacred Attention appears, and then all of me serves that, obeys that."

"Instead of ego, you mean."

"Ego is that which separates me from others. When I become more interested in this connection with something precious, ego and judgment melt away."

"For me it's like trying to swim in sulfuric acid. As soon as Tom opens his mouth, I want him to shut up."

"So there is a reaction. You allow it to be but at the same time come back to this centeredness. What is this reaction? Is it important? And perhaps you see that it is nothing—fear of this or wishing for that. But the primary thing is this relation with an energy. You can find that place in you that can let it be."

LeClair looks out the window; he lowers his gaze as he turns toward Nicholas. No words, yet what is felt then is an intense light arising. It gives Nicholas a different sense of himself—in a way, he doesn't recognize himself. Even Tom can be there in This!

Back at the shed, Nicholas finds Tom sanding the workbench.

"Looks great, doesn't it?" says Tom. "Sorry we didn't use your plan. This is just better. Hooks to hang tools and a bin for every kind of nail and screw. Does that make sense?"

That annoying question. Reply? An impulse comes, way out on the periphery, to speak up…. *Or not.* For the first time, a spaciousness in him permits a choice. *I don't have to be right.* Why say anything? Nicholas is so attracted to stay joined with the finer energy, nothing else is as important. *Go deeper. Better for both.*

On Saturday morning at breakfast, Nicholas listens closely when LeClair confirms, "The 'I' that thinks, believes, feels this or that—all identification. Nothing belongs to me except that which recognizes my true nature. When I can see this—it is a great liberation. And I come to live under a new influence. This attention in me can know its Source."

After breakfast, LeClair inspects the workbench. Not all projects get finished in a week, but this one did, and they've done a good job; anyone would say so. But LeClair questions the choice of wood, the height. Not what was hoped for, not what was expected. But interesting. There is no pat on the back for a job well done, and in a way, that makes more of an impression on Nicholas.

There's a damp patch of ceiling above the bench. A leak?

Tom climbs up to examine the area. Lifting his arm, he leans his back against the rough-hewn wall.

LeClair says under his breath, "Be careful. You might get a nail up your ass."

Tom doesn't hear. But Nicholas smiles.

On the last evening, the great hall is cleared, piano music plays, and people sit on the floor in a circle around a large empty space. A few get up, move to the center, and begin to whirl like dervishes. At first only those who are experienced participate, moving in synch with the music; the room comes alive with whirling. More people join in— *brave souls*, thinks Nicholas, having never seen anything like it in person. Some stop, stand a moment, and go back to their places to make room for others. It is not expected that everyone spin. One woman's long skirt blooms around her.

How eagerly Tom watches the whirlers in their clockwise turning. All at once he is on his feet, spinning like a dervish, except… too fast for the music—and in the wrong direction! Tom is twirling counterclockwise.

Late that night, after everyone is in bed, Nicholas finds Tom alone in the men's room. "Tom? It's freezing in here."

"I did it wrong."

"What do you mean?" But Nicholas knows.

"I turned to my left instead of my right."

"It doesn't matter. Really. Nobody's thinking about it."

"I can't go to bed. I'll just lie there reliving it. I've tried everything, breathing, counting. I just want to be peaceful again."

They walk to the warm kitchen.

"At lunch when I was speaking and got cut off in front of everyone," says Nicholas, "I suffered a lot with that. You're very sensitized after something like that. You feel totally deflated. It's even difficult to speak to people, deal with people. Suddenly, you're nobody—and you're nobody for a long time. You suffer, until the truth of it dawns on you, that when we have these times of noticing our state, there's Something more here, too." He hasn't realized this until he says it aloud, "We focus on the suffering and the negativity instead of on what has *real* value. Because when we wake up... I guess what I'm saying is..." Nicholas, in the stillness, present and steady, like a nail in wood, "what we feel is ourselves in God."

"Nick...."

"Uh-huh."

"Last year, what I did. So rude. Making fun of you like that, behind your back. I was a jerk. I'm sorry."

On a bench in the kitchen, they sit side by side, like two old combat veterans.

STORY 3

The Only Way Out Is Up

Seymour takes a blow.

"The jungle grows up quickly every day. Must make a path every day. Keep something of this inner secret life alive while in activity in the world." LeClair's words are a call to consciousness. Seymour intends to honor them—and to learn the name of every one of the ninety international guests who have come here to Switzerland to work with LeClair on retreat at his chalet.

It's Seymour's first time on the mountain. His assigned task is to clean out the cupboard in the dining hall to prepare for painting. When he cannot reach the top shelf, he takes the nearby piano bench, steps up onto it—

Crunch. *No!*

He looks around. The room is empty. Quickly he picks up the broken bench and hides it in the closet under some linens.

All day he carries that bench. To break something his first day—and then to cover it up! Where is the Eagle Scout, Order of the Arrow, who after all these years still prides himself on being trustworthy, honest, helpful, brave? *How can I know myself when I pretend to be someone else?*

The next morning in the dining hall, he sits at a table with other artists sketching designs for the cupboard. So many creative types make it hard to agree. The discussion comes haltingly, with seriously hushed tones and knitted brows.

Legs crossed at the knee, Seymour is unaware that under the table his shin moves up-down, up-down. Monasteries make him nervous.

"How about an enneagram?" Someone shows his sketch of the star-like symbol.

"Predictable."

"Something Swiss?"

"Edelweiss? We can do better."

"How about a mural?"

Seymour studies the sketches. Cave art. Smears that go nowhere. A face that looks like a violin. Finally, he says, "Is there a time limit on this thing?" He smiles, flashing his perfect teeth.

"There's a piano recital in here tomorrow night. LeClair wants us to be done by then."

Seymour glances at the space where the missing piano bench needs to be.

Coffee break. The others leave. Empty room. Silence. Are the walls imbued with it? Seymour opens the can of primer and dips his brush. Such a pleasure, gliding paint onto wood. After twenty minutes, he sits back, admiring his work.

LeClair comes in. They have not met yet, but from the doorway he looks at Seymour, then at the cupboard, then back, as if to say, "Oh, that's nice."

But Seymour feels caught—*I must look really puffed up about that cabinet*—and turns away.

At dinner, in response to someone's comment that "sensing one's body makes life real," LeClair's reply is something Seymour has not heard before. "Attention is the only matter that can receive finer influences. But it is not free—taken mostly by thoughts.

It needs a ground—the body—so the attention can stay." He adds, "And it's not just about *my* attention, *put* it there. Let go of old ideas, years and years of them, not go around and around in the same circles. When there is this central attention, nothing else comes ahead of it, not ideas, not instructions."

For the after-dinner presentation, an older man from the States talks about a certain esoteric diagram in various iterations. *Kind of takes the mystery out of it,* thinks Seymour. *The map is not the country.* The longer the talk goes on, the more embarrassing, that this man represents us Americans. Seymour reaches the nadir; he is going under; wave after wave of cerebral exhaustion. Man the lifeboats!

The moment the talk is over, Seymour bolts. Outside, he leans against the building. Go behind the shed for a smoke?

LeClair comes out the door. Stops. Raises the heel of his hand. Gives one quick blow to Seymour's chest—zap!—and walks on.

Instantly everything looks different, everything brand new. In a heightened state Seymour wanders the property. People say goodnight, but no way can he go to bed now. He sits on the low wall at the edge of the terrace. In the valley, village lights are illuminated to make a cross. Something streaks through the sky, then bursts like fireworks— Seymour doesn't know *what* he is looking at. And a life inside him, much higher than the body.

At daybreak he goes to the dining hall to start the espresso machine. Ahead of him on the steps is an old man moving slowly.

"Oh, Seymour," LeClair turns to face him. "So tired. Work all night. No sleep."

Take his arm so he doesn't fall? Just then Seymour has the oddest impression. Behind this appearance of an old man with a two-day-beard, is it…? For show?

Seymour smiles, displaying those beautiful supernatural teeth.

LeClair smiles back. Not at all old. Not at all tired.

"I'm sorry you have to deal with us Americans," Seymour says. "We're so in our heads."

"You think the Americans are bad." He puts his palm to his forehead as if in pain. "You don't know the French."

How is it that now, in front of LeClair, Seymour is acutely aware, as if a mirror is turned powerfully on himself. And yet, no desire for anything to be different. "I did something terrible," he confesses. "I broke the piano bench."

"So good you told me. Now we can fix it," says LeClair. "Sometimes people don't say, and we don't know."

I suffered so much for nothing!

At the espresso machine, LeClair sips his coffee through a sugar cube. "Do you miss American coffee?"

"Yes."

"Chef is driving to town to buy meat. Special butcher shop. Go with him. Get coffee."

Seymour is flattered; new "campers" rarely get to leave the premises lest they act strange in front of the neighbors. *Keep something of this inner life alive....*

At his desk LeClair draws a map on a scrap of paper and hands it to Seymour. "Be back by 11. No later. Very important."

Chef's car speeds along steep drops, hairpin turns. Around every bend, a tour bus too wide for the road. Seymour white-knuckles it down the mountain, foot braced hard against the car floor.

The city's outskirts look psychedelic. Stark grey industrial buildings. A giant furniture factory against an electric-blue sky. And… is that a McDonald's? Seymour hadn't realized how altered his state is. Things look surreal.

At the supermarket, a gigantic yellow squash. Seymour lingers among the 'shrooms. Chef hurries him to the coffee aisle. It's 9:45.

In the car, at the designated rotary, Seymour takes out the scrap of paper.

They drive, looking everywhere for the right street but can't find it. Chef says, "We're going to be late."

They travel a quarter mile to the next rotary. No good. And to a third. Around again and again in circles, always ending up in the same place. *Keep something alive….*

"Can't we go to another butcher?" says Seymour. It's 10:15.

"You have to buy from the same family."

Seymour looks at the paper. Turns it.

Back to the first rotary.

There it is. The butcher shop.

"It was here all the time," Seymour says, looking at the scrap of paper. "He drew the map upside down."

"Of course."

It's 11 a.m. when they return. Seymour walks down the pebbly path to the chalet. What a sight! Over one shoulder, a clear plastic bag filled with bloody meat; over the other, a giant sack of toilet paper rolls.

LeClair meets him in the courtyard. "Americans use a lot of toilet paper," he says as the two walk to the kitchen.

For the rest of the week, unassigned to a project, Seymour roams the property helping where needed; he is especially welcomed by the women in the kitchen when there is stressing over meal preparations.

On the last night the men alone are tasked with cooking dinner. Seymour says, "Let's make chefs' hats out of paper to wear while we're serving." Cheerfulness, the plainest sign of wisdom.

"No, no," scoffs Lecture Guy. "Not appropriate."

"There's no time," says Chef.

But Mr. Congeniality finds craft paper

and gleefully begins making four dervish-like stovepipe hats, round, white, and two-feet tall. A few of the women help him.

The dinner bell rings. Just inside the entrance to the dining hall, Seymour is one of four "chefs" in their toques standing behind the serving station.

LeClair walks in. At the sight of them, he grins. Instantly, he goes up on his tiptoes! He does a little dance, wiggling his fingers, smiling. It's like a sparkler going off. Heads turn. He whispers something to the pianist who pounds out a comical tune.

Seymour is so happy that we are free enough to play!

The next day, on the way to the airport, Seymour and friends stop at a café. The salade verte is placed in the center of the table. They all look at it, then at each other. Big grins, for they are all seeing it the same way at the same time. This salad glows. Lustrous lettuce. Ah, the splendor of it all!

All the Other Voices

*Angie can't find the right
note to sing.*

Angie forgets to bring a sleeping bag to the retreat in the Alps, and with only a borrowed blanket, she is cold on the mattress on the floor. She puts on all the warm clothes she's brought. The rest of us in the dorm are sleeping just fine; she wants to be like that, but now it's hopeless. Chilled, just off the plane, surely she will catch cold precisely when she needs to be at her best for these few precious days of inner work with LeClair. Tears on her cheeks burn like drops of hot solder. Will there ever be a night she doesn't cry?

Darkness presses in at the uncurtained window.

She writes down that sentence on the notepad by her pillow. She has taken to composing sentences in her head, for the novel, to keep from crying.

What to do now that the diamond edge is lost?

How to tread these waters, mindful of their treasures?

The ball of pressure in her chest means she won't be able to get back to sleep; she never can. She reaches for a flashlight and reads under the covers her little yellow paperback of Zen parables: A MAN, CHASED BY A TIGER, WENT OVER A CLIFF, CLUTCHED A VINE, HANGING BY A THREAD; MICE GNAWED AT IT; TIGER ABOVE, TIGER BELOW; WITHIN REACH, A RIPE STRAWBERRY; HOW SWEET IT TASTES!

It is for that taste that she has traveled all the way from Portland to Switzerland. It seems a small journey compared with others who have to go a thousand steps on their knees to arrive at such a special place. She plans to throw herself into physical labor, dishwashing, cooking, cleaning, to go against her natural resistance—the professor in her would rather sit and write—and in this way, pay for her keep.

Walking downstairs the next morning,

hair askew, she feels like an outsider on an alien planet. The women in the kitchen take little notice. "What are you doing here?" their glances seem to say.

"What can I help with?" Angie asks.

The Swiss women know each other, know the place well, where things are kept, how things are done, toiling away with noiseless efficiency. "You must look around and see," the reply descends upon her.

The cold shoulder, the closed hand.

Or is she mistaken? At breakfast, a choice of sugary cereals. Angie forgoes them all; she needs protein. At least the discussion fortifies. LeClair speaks of contact with a heavenly quality and an earthly quality, and "how extraordinary to be in both at the same time." But it is heaven alone that interests Angie now.

The women meet to assign chores for the day. Paulina, an elder in the discipline, reads from a list. "Not enough people for dish-washing."

"Get the men to do it."

Giggles and nods.

"Does anyone know how to sew?" asks

Paulina.

Angie raises her hand.

"Thank you." Paulina writes down the name. "Oh, but you're already signed up for two teams. Won't that be too much?"

Angie washes ninety breakfast bowls and scours the men's bathroom. A light July rain turns into a cold downpour soaking everything. Men make a wet mess every time they come in. Her task is to mop the entranceway. It's lined with shelves on which empty silver pitchers, their handles all aligned in the same direction, are being carefully placed by two women. Angie grudgingly cleans around their feet. She'd mop away the people if she could.

In comes a big galoot with mud on his boots.

"Don't you see you're bringing in all this dirt!" Angie puts down towels as floor mats. She stations herself at the doorway, trailing after yellow slickers, cleaning the floor a dozen times.

The air is troubled by an inhospitable wind.

At coffee break, no one comes to sit next to her. People seem... cool to her. They pass the chocolate in the other direction so there is none left for her. Worse—of all times—her PMS is making her, as she confesses to Paulina, "really crazy."

Outside LeClair's room, Angie waits on the bench. When it's her time to go in, she cannot bring herself to speak about what she has come all this way to ask him. Instead, she describes what happened a few days earlier in France. Angie had marveled at the tidal island Abbey of Mont St. Michel rising out of earth and water. That she was actually standing there, seeing it in the morning light—how lucky to be living in this body!

She tells LeClair, "I received something. I suddenly felt it's a miracle to be alive—and this love for everything that lives. When I have an experience like that, I feel I understand something, but not in words. Is that true or is it ego?"

"Do you know when it's hot or cold outside?" he says. "The way you can know the temperature, you can know the truth."

"It felt holy."

"You have been in it many times," he says. "Align more and more with this greater force, something absolutely greater than myself, this sacred energy coming into me. Love is one aspect of it. Compassion can come through me—compassion for my parts, too."

Angie exhales heavily, like she just moved the piano.

LeClair's voice, an invitation. "Suddenly, there is contact with a higher energy that brings more and more a feeling of belonging, of being part of that. Let this feeling for consciousness arise."

"I forget. I lose it. I have too many emotions. Too many reactions."

"Something goes and returns. That's the way it is. Every hour, to align. See the sense of 'I AM' and what happens to take me away—and the return."

"But I behave badly—others treat me badly...."

"We can't help making mistakes. It can't be held against us. Just like you love a toddler, you love people despite the messes. You've got to let people love you."

"I want *them* to be different, *me* to be different. I have all this self-doubt."

"It never goes away."

To hear *him* say those words, and so matter-of-factly—surprising—freeing. Like he's talking about his toes: yes, sure, always there, no problem—*when this other dimension opens.*

Back at the sinks, now how gingerly Angie washes the dishes. When a man brings more plates to clean, she sees the quality of attention in him, wants to aid that, not be an obstacle.

The day has a little light in it now.

She even asks to join the choral group practicing for Saturday night's performance. No singer, she just wants to be in the Unity with others.

At the center of our semicircle of men and women taking direction from Paulina, Angie leans toward us altos, to hear the notes. She can't quite find the strand in the four-part harmony of "Tiebie Payom," a prayer in Ukrainian. The piano plays the altos' line twice. Will Angie ever get it? She mouths the words, pretending to sing.

Later in the kitchen Angie carries in groceries. Twenty dozen eggs. She asks the woman in charge, "Can I possibly boil some eggs for myself and leave them in the fridge? I'm pre-diabetic. It would help me so much if I could have protein in the morning."

"How many?"

"A dozen?"

"A dozen!"

Angie gets six. She hard-boils them and puts them in a paper bag with her name on it in the crowded fridge.

The following morning the bag is out on the counter. The new woman-in-charge scolds Angie: what if everyone set aside their own blah blah blah. Angie is showing anger in the colors of her aura.

A wound, making the least offense poison.

The week goes like that, up and down. On Friday an announcement comes: Saturday is sauna day. Women in the morning, men in the afternoon. Angie's first-ever sauna! She anticipates the jokes, the camaraderie. But Saturday morning she gets the news: she will not be using the sauna, she will be serving. In the kitchen she assembles fruit platters for others to enjoy after the heat. Up the stairs she totes plates of orange wedges and cantaloupe chunks. In the dorm, women lounge in robes and give each other foot massages. Angie replenishes pitchers of iced tea.

In the shadows, a chill wind pushes against the wall of her loneliness.

Just before noon, Angie puts on her robe, hoping to shower before the men take over the bathrooms.

Paulina is clearing wet towels from the racks. "Oh, sorry," she intercepts Angie, "no more hot water. It needs time to replenish." Seeing her expression, Paulina says, "Come. We'll go sit and relax."

The two women spread towels on the balcony off the women's dorm. With a plate of melon before them, they sun themselves.

From the cloistered chalet, the valley spreads like a washed-out quilt.

Paulina says, "You look sad."

That this stranger sees what others do not....

Somehow Angie can say the words she has not yet said aloud. "My husband died. Two months ago. It was sudden. It changed the way I look at everything." Watery eyes. "I'm a crying machine these days. It's like I don't want to be in the world anymore."

"My husband is off-planet."

Odd way to....

"It's been a year," says Paulina. "He's just with me in a different way now."

"What do you mean?"

"At first it took me a while to realize I can talk to him and he actually responds, in my head. I shouldn't be saying any of—"

"Please...."

Both women lean back, looking at the mountains.

Paulina says, "I'd be sure it was him, then later I'd doubt it. It seemed too good to be true. But things happened that were so... amazing... I just knew it was him showing me he's still with me. I mean, I couldn't make up these things."

"What does he say?"

"'Different, but wonderful.' He said it many times those first few weeks. He was giving me a way to think about it all— that even though he's not in the body we're together." She pauses. "Maybe, like LeClair says, we really are multidimensional crea- tures. It feels that way."

"How do you know it's your husband?"

Paulina giggles. "Because he's still so good at minimizing my problems."

"Does it get better... or...."

"If my thoughts go off on their own when a memory is triggered, there's tears. But when he's just helped me with something—just know it's him—I thank him for taking such good care of me. And he says, 'Where else would I be?'"

"He loves you."

"Or *is* love." Paulina turns to Angie. "You've got to let yourself grieve. It's good that you came here. There's something very precious here. We can become sensitive to a quality in us, among us. We can serve something greater, not of this earth. And for this, you and I can be useful."

A southerly breeze arises, and subsides, like an exhalation.

"I felt a stillness like this," says Angie, "sitting by my husband while he was passing. The hospital sounds stopped. We were in a bubble of silence."

"Amazing grace."

Angie gives out a little laugh. "Oh, so that's what it means."

The chimes from the village church sound the noon hour. As Angie listens, her in-breath and out-breath align with each note ringing: I... AM... I... AM... I... AM.... And it's delicious there on the balcony, with her bare legs outstretched.

All her problems, what do they matter now, as she sits like this in the sun?

That evening at the last-night celebration, in a festive white kurta embroidered with tiny green vines, Angie admires the decorations. The dining room's four corners abound with alpine flowers. A freshly painted mural enlivens the far wall. Oriental rugs comprise a stage. Women in long dresses and men in collared shirts drink from small glasses of Armagnac. All during dinner, though, Angie takes out and studies her sheet music, especially that place where the altos come in alone but have never gotten it right.

"More Armagnac?" offers the man on her right.

"No, thank you. I don't want to get drunk."

"You're having too much fun already."

A little smile. Her stomach, a hollow.

The choral group is called. Angie takes

her place on stage. LeClair is close by. She sees him. The pianist begins.

When Angie starts to sing, she finds she can listen to all the voices and blend with them. Her face beams. The altos come in perfectly. Voices in harmony as enriching to the moment as if infinite overtones were added to the primary note of ordinary perception. It's a heavenly choir.

Overhead, a vast veiling cloud moves away, revealing a room with no ceiling. She is able to reach toward the light, releasing something buried, a new life rising.

More tears to come? Yes. But oh, how she sings out, the One in her that is full of joy.

The Masks Keep Falling

*Laurence identifies
with his role.*

Watching the in-flight movie, Laurence wants to hold his young sweetie's hand but cannot. The seatbelt sign comes on. Landing in Geneva. Because of a bandaged palm, he struggles to fasten the buckle. Juliet leans over and clicks it in. He smiles. She smiles. They kiss like enamored fish.

"So fun!" says Juliet, eyes shining.

"Too bad Cole couldn't come." What a relief. Now Laurence can have Juliet all to himself for a whole week, free of their mutual "friend." And in the sublime atmosphere of the retreat. Won't she be impressed!

"Cole is coming. He's got an audition for a film, but after that—"

"He told me meditation isn't his—"

"He sees how happy you are every summer when you come back from these things, he wants to meet LeClair, you mention him so much—"

"Is that what you guys were talking about backstage? Seemed very intense." It was the exact moment that—bam!—the hand got injured. "What were you—"

"Nothing."

"Nothing."

The flight attendant comes down the aisle. Fasten your seatbelts.

MONDAY

Clouds obscure the Matterhorn. It's the first full day of the retreat. At the chalet Laurence waits on the terrace for Juliet. She comes out of the sewing room. Because Laurence has mended many a costume for his theater troupe in New York, she shows him where the elbow is worn through in the Tibetan-style shirt. He instantly recognizes it as LeClair's favorite, a signature garment on him. Juliet threads the needle, hands the shirt to Laurence, and goes back inside.

Laurence sews with his good hand. Men walk by, hauling bags of cement. "What are you doing?" their looks seem to say. But he works like a surgeon, focused on every stitch. He repairs the spot that had almost no fabric.

He brings the shirt to LeClair's room. The door is ajar. He knocks, looks in. What catches his eye: assorted full-face theatrical masks on the wall. He places the garment on the doorknob and leaves.

At dinner LeClair is wearing the shirt. The sight makes Laurence happy, so much so that when Cole walks in, the world feels expanded enough to include him.

"Cole!" Juliet hugs him and makes room so he can sit down. Her welcoming hand on his knee.

"You're here," says Laurence. But the mask wears thin.

Food is served.

Cole says, "So, Larry, off the top of your head, what does this place give you?"

"A reason to *be*."

TUESDAY

"What you wish for is here, now," says

LeClair at the breakfast gathering.

Laurence turns to Juliet with a smile, but she's looking across the room at Cole—and the pretty mademoiselle sitting next to him.

A woman says, "I feel lost."

In LeClair's facial expression, a listening for the nature of the difficulty. He says, "Stay just exactly as I am. Let the impressions come in. There is an energy in me that can accept." He is interrupted by the woman clarifying what she means. He responds, "It is possible precisely when 'I cannot.' 'I cannot,' and I become so poor, so receptive. And so it is received. The Attention can flow down, fill me, so there is nothing else but to *be*."

More questions about difficulties. Laurence hears LeClair say, "Sometimes I'm like a rat. Goes to one door—shut. To another door—shut. To another door—shut. So it accepts, sits there, and begins to *be*."

Someone asks about "the madness, the crimes against the earth and each other," and the impossibility of "accepting."

"Sadness, perhaps, which arises," says LeClair. "Pity. Compassion maybe. See this suffering—me—others. Deep wounds. Yet healing takes place from this energy when I'm in relation with it. From it can come my best action in the world, my best action for others."

But Laurence's attention is engaged elsewhere: Cole and Juliet, looking at each other.

WEDNESDAY

"We'll have a play on the last night," LeClair announces at lunch. "Laurence will direct."

Juliet turns to Laurence—good for you! He is flattered about being put in charge, but right away he thinks *no time, no script,* and he'll have to direct people who have been with LeClair for decades.

After lunch, Juliet vanishes. Later, in the basement, Laurence locates her standing by the washing machine.

"Hey," she says softly.

It has been only three hours, yet he's lovestruck at the sight of her. "I've been looking for you."

"Towels," she says. "Almost done. What's up?"

"Saturday night. The show." But now,

seeing her, he doesn't want to go into it. The way her hair falls over her shoulders and down the curve of her breasts....

"Call a meeting for people who want to work on it," she says. "Isn't it lucky that Cole's here."

...And a mouth that is loveliest when she smiles.

Laurence moves closer.

"Improv is your thing," she says. Spin cycle. "You're great at it. You're perfect."

"It's my only flaw." A mischievous fingertip hovers over her waist. "I'm going to have to... poke you now—"

She bats away his hand. "Not here."

The washer stops. Juliet loads towels into a basket.

Wilted tulips.

Laurence carries the basket to the clothesline. Outside, the peaks blush with the softer colors of sunset.

THURSDAY

"Who's a writer?" Laurence asks the volunteers.

Hands go up. Everyone agrees about needing a script. But Laurence has something else in mind. He noticed, that first morning in LeClair's room, the masks on the wall. He asks people close to LeClair, "Can we use the masks?"

"No way." "They're special." "Forget it." No one will request permission.

So he does.

"Yes, of course." LeClair explains how the masks were made years ago for a project. Then he says, "How is the week going?"

"People are doing better," Laurence reports. "It's just... some personal stuff... hard to accept." He dismisses it with "Jealous as an eight-year-old."

"Acceptance is 'energetical.'"

Mechanically Laurence nods "yes."

LeClair takes it further. "Acceptance as we talk of it now is preliminary psychological acceptance. It's okay, but when the real thing appears, this higher energy, we are completely transformed. Not that 'I' accept but that I am related to this energy that accepts all."

Ten minutes more of conversation and Laurence is brimful, and excited to return to the cast. Now he will do what he's always wanted, to create without worrying about the result. He lays out the masks. "Never mind a script. Let's try something. Pick one."

Each person chooses a mask and puts it on. No two people reach for the same one, and all are taken.

"This is great." "So fun!" "I wish I could wear this all the time."

The instant Laurence puts on his mask—exhilaration! The idea comes: "Let's do the week in review."

Somehow freed behind the masks, the actors brainstorm moments ripe for sendup. The laughter gets so loud that someone comes to tell them to quiet down. *But it feels good to laugh at ourselves.* So much to make fun of: vanity, swagger, pretension.... Jealousy?

That night, after rehearsal, Cole and Juliet are ascloseasthis. Laurence finds them cozy in the kitchen drinking tea. Helpless at the sight, he launches into a Juliet-and-I-have-been-together-forever spiel. He goes through their past like a travel agent. "...We're in Ibiza, skinny-dipping off the rocks, and we look up, and there are a dozen

Spanish police with rifles."

"You've done such great things," says Cole. He runs his hand through his hair like a hunky leading man in a Hallmark movie.

Juliet butters her bread on both sides.

"Honey?" Cole speaks to her as if they are the only people in the room.

Juliet shakes her head no. Yawns. "Long day."

His cue. "So I'll say goodnight." Cole exits.

"More tea?" says Laurence.

"I don't want more tea." She looks like the attorney for the prosecution. "What was that?"

"Hmm?" Never say die.

"You don't trust me. You want to control me," she demonizes him to justify her behavior.

FRIDAY

"Larry? Larry!" Juliet shoves him in the shoulder to get his attention as they walk to her dorm in the dark. "You're so weird. The rehearsal went great. Everything is fine."

The wind is blowing in several directions

at once.

"Is it?" With all the scenes playing in his head, need he ever go to the movies?

"Don't worry," she tells him. "It'll work out. It always does."

"Maybe for—"

"Not just—"

"You and Cole?" Laurence changes lanes without signaling.

"He certainly has the touch," she says.

"What?"

"Timing. Comic timing," she adds. "What'd you think I—"

"Nothing."

"Nothing."

"You want to be with him," he doesn't say.

"You're such a pain," she doesn't.

They're at her door. Laurence is practiced in a certain kind of observation. "Tell me."

"Cole can get me a film in L.A. And he's someone you can trust."

"Well, he wouldn't steal a red-hot stove."

"More opportunity. Better for us."

"You and him?" Into the ditch.

"You and me, silly. Leave New York. See what's out there." She puts her fingertip to his mouth—no more talk. "Hey… it's late. I have to go.… Whatever are you going to do without me?" The flirty smile does not comfort.

Laurence leans in for a goodnight kiss, but they do not move into that other country.

Sitting in his bunk in the men's tent, Laurence decides he hates the mountains. They are like walls. Juliet. Cole. How dare they. *What I should have said.…* What she said, what Cole said. *She looks at him the way she used to look at me.* Even as it all replays, it feels pornographic—not fitting for this place.

His bandaged hand. The gauze. He rips it off.

He closes his eyes. No way to fix. He's nobody to her now.

Sometimes I'm like a rat.…

Nothing to be done.

Breathe. Just breathe.

Turn toward the Life sitting here now.

SATURDAY

A masked dryad in forest green plays the flute. The final night's performance has begun. For "The Seven Days" of the retreat, Laurence takes the role of Whipping Boy carrying everybody's bags. In ones and twos, exhibitionist incongruous personages of every type say their piece. Flirtation, argument, flattery, envy, all wear masks suitable for the occasion. Like molecules, little groups come together and split apart, speculating about God, speculating about death, speculating about the platter gone missing from the fridge. When Cole does his bit, he gets the biggest laughs. And between scenes, the whispering of the Greek chorus:

Apart from all my stories, who am I?

For the finale, standing in a line across the front of the room, the cast put their hands to their faces and, all together in one measured gesture, s-l-o-w-l-y lower their masks.

It is a striking moment—for them, too, because suddenly they are exposed. They place the masks on the ground and file out.

Then: Quick! Quick! In runs Juliet, picks up her mask, and runs out. The capper. Yes, better take that mask along, just in case.

Applause. Congratulations. People gather around Laurence. A hug from Juliet; it is a cold feeling.

Not a word from LeClair. Of course it's not his way to pump up egos—but Laurence would so love to hear something. *Isn't that the way it always goes? Wanting to be somebody, when really, we could be so free.*

NINE MONTHS LATER

New York, New York. Opening night of the off-Broadway play Laurence staged using masks he collected during the year. He walks to the theater. At that moment a car moves along the avenue toward Barrow Street carrying someone special. The trees are budding. The weather has turned warmer with the promise of summer.

From behind the curtain, Laurence scans the audience. Not here.

After the performance, in the lobby, an unexpected sight. Is it Juliet and Cole? Is it hurtful how happy she looks?

No. Not them.

Among well-wishers chatting in groups: LeClair. Here in New York, and at the play! Laurence is thrilled.

But LeClair walks right by him. Disappointing—of course LeClair meets so many people—

"Laurence."

That voice. Like someone reaching down his throat and gripping his heart.

The two men discuss theater, and it's obvious how much LeClair loves it too. All at once Laurence is deeply glad. It's as if a being of light has come through the door and surrounds them. Nothing to get; nothing is wanted. Here, fully himself like this, speaking with LeClair like this—it's more than enough!

And then LeClair says, "I once saw another group do theater in masks. In the end, they took off their masks. It was such a strong impression."

Half-Baked or Fully Cooked

*Things heat up for Mary—
but what about Jason?*

The taxi moves along the narrow road by the canal, up to the striped pillars on either side of the driveway, through the entrance, past the house, to the parking lot behind—all in the middle of endless flat fields where horses graze in the distance. No one around. In her eagerness, Mary has arrived too early at the retreat. Her husband Jason drops her off and takes the taxi into town "to explore."

Crossing the street, Mary sits on a bench by the canal. Low-bending branches bow to the river's flow. Soon the light around her comes alive; a fine energy self-selects into prominence. Now it doesn't matter what came before. She is here. It is Saturday noon. Holland in September. Grey skies. Cold wind. Too cold to sit outside for long.

Upstairs in the women's dorm, one person is asleep in the end bunk, so deeply that she is not disturbed by footsteps and voices. A long room with ten single beds, five on a side, each with its little table and lamp. At one end, the bathroom with two showers and four sinks. At the other, the door to another dorm. Choose bed, figure out what to unpack and what to hang on the communal rack in the middle of the room. Locate the closet with the quilts and pillows. Make the bed. Go to the main house and help.

Hours later, many arrivals, from different countries. Jason is back. What about dinner? Not until the man in charge appears, and LeClair is delayed. At eight, bread and cheese are brought out. At nine, it's pouring. Jason eats Cliff Bars in his dorm. Mary worries about the poor impression all of this is making on him; after all, he was reluctant to come. Back home Jason has stopped going with her to their weekly meditation group; she hopes being here will renew his interest. She would have preferred returning in summer to LeClair's chalet in Switzerland—so bright, high up in the mountains—but no matter. She can't wait to give LeClair her gift, an afghan she crocheted for him sitting by the wood stove during the long New England winter. She has such expectations!

At ten, people still congregate in the main building but she decides to go to her dorm across the driveway and brush her teeth while the bathroom is empty. She puts on her raincoat and walks to the back hall so she can slip away. As she reaches the door—

In walks LeClair. They are alone. He greets her with a kiss on the forehead. Just seeing his face…. Now everything will be fine!

The next morning in the kitchen, Mary hears, "Americans can't cook." How rude. And how wrong. "We can cook," she announces to the women while big pots of water boil on temperamental stoves.

At a long table, the kitchen team prepares munchies for break. What's on the menu? For Mary, it's "a central attention," as LeClair puts it. She is determined not to get pulled away by anything that happens. She creates a mosaic of carrots and celery on the platter.

Suddenly, the atmosphere and feeling at

the table change—

LeClair is behind her, looking at the plate.

She chirps, "What do you think?" She smells terrific.

He picks up a carrot, puts it in his mouth. "Could be crisper."

She's thinking, *Soon we'll have more to talk about than carrots!*

Just then Jason walks past the window. In his usual contractor-mode, he easily shoulders a two-by-four. LeClair comments, "He looks happy to be here." Good to hear; she hadn't noticed.

Despite the fact that she is American (or because of it), Mary is put in charge of lunch. Please note that the kitchen at these retreats is never just a kitchen: it's an arena. They lock the fridge. Difficulties are routine. Today it's that the food shoppers will not return in time, and eighty guests await lunch. The pantry and fridge are depleted of the usual pâté, kefir and beef, clams and melons, eggs and lamb, spinach, ossenwurst, herring, wheat germ, sponge cake, capers. All Mary finds are hard peaches, egg noodles, six tomatoes the size of chestnuts, white cauliflower, and some Parmesan. Not even an onion, the lynchpin of Western civilization.

While the cooks stand around, Mary goes outside to the kitchen garden. Cows sit lumped in a field. Finding nothing, and not ready to face the others, she crosses the street to the canal, hoping it will work its magic. In the stream or up the creek? But she must go back; she must not be dismayed by that pasty pale meal. She boils the peaches to ripen them.

An older woman comes into the kitchen. "Why are you all asleep? Why is this all white?" Immediately she makes a mustard dressing for the cauliflower.

At one o'clock, the lunch bell rings.

Insisting that LeClair likes his noodles *al dente*, one of the cooks steps in saying "It's done" and pours cold water into the pots too soon. Big clumps of noodles stuck together. Some of it is salvageable, but there won't be as much. Mary takes back the regular lunch plates and brings out small ones.

LeClair comes into the kitchen. He takes a forkful, puts it in his mouth and—spits it out!

Heads turn. "We're so sorry." "We messed up."

It is—and for a second, this is how Mary sees it—*exactly like theater.*

But then LeClair raises his voice in disgust.

A young woman is in tears.

Mary blurts out, "You're making her cry. Don't do that." But to scold *him*!

At lunch, though, LeClair looks pleased. "This meal has struggle in it." In front of everyone, he praises the cooks.

All for show? A test? To stay with "a central attention" no matter what. Will the menu ever be the meal?

Disappointing for Mary—such a small thing, but her world contracts to "i'm-not-good-enough," so easily believed. *Not enough presence. Too much ego. Reactive. Helpless.* A few found breaths—but it's a fitful night's sleep.

With new resolve, she tries again the next day to be as continuously aware as possible in the kitchen. For the midday meal, the Head Cook instructs her to use olive oil on the roast. Mary puts on a little, as she might at home, but upon inspection, Cook makes her pour a whole bottle over the meat, saying, "We always use olive oil to make the food taste better."

The women are called to a meeting with LeClair—except someone needs to watch over the food cooking.

Mary sits by the gas stove, giant pots simmering.

Suddenly—smoke!

Mary opens the oven door—

Flames!

She grabs a box of salt. Empties it onto the fiery roast. Slams-shut the door. Heat off. Fire out? Dare she look?

Jason! Help! Heart beats so fast. She hasn't given him a thought all day (and he's up on the roof, thatching), but now she sends for him.

He checks the oven. Smoke and char.

"They made me pour all this oil on the meat. I would never do that. They left me here by myself. I don't know this kitchen," she says. "It's so much harder here, below sea level. Not like up on the mountain." How she wanted him to love it.

He puts his arms around her. "You got this."

As soon as the women return, Mary goes to LeClair. Surely he will issue instructions: there needs to be a second person in the kitchen at all times. But he says little, just that he is pleased the fire was taken care of. Their meeting is brief.

She complains to Jason. "He didn't do anything about it." But to feel angry at LeClair!

"Maybe he will."

"I didn't expect this. It's usually not like this."

"It's fine. Don't worry about *me*," says Jason, knowing her so well.

Back at the cutting table, heads of lettuce languish on the block. Mary tells the women, "What happened with the roast isn't good. We need at least two people in the kitchen at all times."

The women agree. They thank her. They praise her quick action. They do everything but flash a peace sign at her.

But she joins the sewing team. Heavy rain sets in. She is glad for the sound of it. Just listen to the rain and be.

When Mary finishes sewing some drapes, she is told to deliver them to LeClair's room. *Bring the afghan.* Surely he will love it: attention inhabits every stitch. This time she will talk to him about more pleasant matters. She is eager for the look on his face when she hands him the throw.

"I've made this for you," she says, sitting down with him.

LeClair drops it on the bed behind him and says... nothing more about it. "My wife... passed," he tells Mary, tears in his eyes.

"You must miss her very much."

A second later, he is composed. "How has your work been going?" He's asking about inner work for consciousness.

Of course what he wants to talk about is more important—*but what about the afghan?* Sunny yellow laced with sky blue. And so soft....

Another short meeting.

Walking her to the door, LeClair says casually, "What a wonderful husband I have."

What? Why say that?

The words replay in her mind as she fills pitchers of water for dinner. She decides LeClair isn't like anyone else—never does what you expect. What's important to you is not important to him in the same way. *But he's always present—and that's all that matters.*

The next day Mary is back in the kitchen making the apple tarts. The large oven is in use so she decides not to wait for it but to try the small one. She is warned that the top shelf burns the food and the bottom under-cooks it. The tarts look perfect going in, but when they come out, half are scorched, half are raw. She does not want to serve LeClair anything bad, so she dumps it all in the gar-bage. People throw their cigarette butts on it.

But what to do for dessert? She doesn't want to ask for the key to the walk-in fridge and have to explain, so instead she checks the small refrigerator. The cheese storage area glows self-promotingly.

Mary brings out the brie.

In the dining hall, LeClair asks, "Where are the apple tarts?"

"They got ruined," says Mary. "I put them in the garbage."

"Let's see what they're like. Why don't you get them?"

Mary refuses. He insists. She goes to the kitchen, digs out the tarts, brushes off the ashes, and brings them; she really wants to drop them on the floor.

"Go ahead. Serve them," says LeClair.

She cuts up the tarts, put the slices on little plates, and hands them out.

LeClair takes a bite. "Not bad."

Everyone else takes a bite—oh, yes, fine—and eats the tarts. Not Mary. Nothing could make her eat those tarts.

LeClair leans toward her and whispers, "See how people are."

Later she tells Jason, "I never know what he means."

"Sure you do."

She finishes cleaning the kitchen just before 5 p.m. It's her favorite time of day because she gets to go to her small-group meeting with LeClair. She enjoys slipping off her shoes outside and entering the little windowless meditation room, a sacred space. All is quiet. And LeClair is there, with that look on his face that she loves, this other-worldly expression as he gazes toward the doorway left open to the light.

Someone asks a question. LeClair says, "Perhaps there is no inclination to turn inward. Let it be. Just watch. The power of attention more and more can fill the body."

Halfway through the meeting, Mary wants to speak so LeClair will look her way, but after the stressful day and sitting so still in that close space, she feels her eyelids get heavy—chin drops—eyes jerk open. Eyelids droop again—chin drops—head twitch. She presses fingernails into palm to keep from physically falling asleep.

And then it happens. LeClair's voice, like adrenaline. "…To join with That which is always within me. It is always there—doesn't need energy, doesn't take energy. But when I am joined with it, great energy enlivens me…."

Contact.

Light brightening wide. Not at all the "self" she is usually aware of. Tiredness gone. Every breath. And LeClair's words, received without comment. "…How to pass from ordinary life to this sensitivity immediately with no bridge? Really empty. And quiet. Let the flow of Attention permeate, animate. Somehow—you pass. You don't know, but somehow you pass...."

It surprises her that nothing need change except where the attention is. If even one person, during the group, threads the labyrinth to find the way out of suffering, then....

Mary steps outside. The delicious scent of rain in the air. The quiet, so striking. Walking across the driveway, she notices debris from the storm. She gets a broom. Just sweeping. Light flickers through the treetops. Limbs of silence.

From the doorway, Jason waves to her. His smile says, Shine big.

What a wonderful husband I have. How has she not appreciated it before, the way in which he has set the tone for their marriage—forged an unspoken pact between them—never to say the unkind thing out of impatience, and so give only the best to each other. He's a master at this. *Because I'm not easy.*

The final morning, as people depart, Jason offers to stay late "if you still want to speak with LeClair." But Mary is told that LeClair is no longer meeting with anyone; he is resting before the new arrivals at five. Everywhere she looks, still so much to do to put the house in order. Mary loads the washer, hangs pillowcases on the clothesline, takes down towels, hour after hour in the afternoon sun. The fields glisten. White swan with a black beak on a green lawn. All here in the swish of a horse's tail. She isn't thinking about LeClair anymore. The feeling the week has created in her... she is happy if she speaks with him, happy if she doesn't. And this other thing she hoped to experience with him, now by the fields it feels just the same as with him, yet it is in her—

"Mary," LeClair calls from the doorway.

He brings her into the hall, to the wood stove, and shows her a beautiful object. It is rectangular, metallic brown, about eight inches wide, with scrollwork, and an oval opening at the center. He explains how, in winter, this bed-warmer "lies on top of the stove to heat up."

He hands it to her, a gift. "And then, it will warm you."

STORY 7

Dancing in the Moonlight

Irene takes a leap of faith.

Irene grew up on the African continent as the only child of missionaries. She read the Bible in the mission house and played with bugs in the backyard. Her circumstances became a source of secret pride: the thrill of making do, the ecstasy of the empty cupboard. Her parents moved so often she never made friends. Nature was her only companion.

And so it is in Switzerland. Although she has come on retreat especially to work with LeClair, once here all she wants is to be with the mountains. She is obsessed with them. The first night, despite being told not to, she takes her sleeping bag outside. Even shivering she feels it's worth it, for there at dawn: the Matterhorn, Mamma Matta, pink around the edges, horn in majesty over the

Swiss countryside.

By mid-week, though, the mountains of-fer little solace; she is worn out. "If only I'd come when I was younger," she tells me. "I'm 76. I'm too old for this." Late nights with the dorm lights always left on. Blow-dryers at dawn. Six a.m. sittings. July sun beating down on her in the garden. Overnights: a series of naps punctuated by rashy bouts of nerve-itch torture. Mealtimes: the bricks-and-mortar diet of bread-and-cheese. *Do I dare eat a peach?* Seated next to her, always someone with a cough. And who is this mys-terious bunkmate who is in bed after her and up before her, still a stranger after three days?

"It's hard here," she says to me. "I drift around grumpy all day thinking this shouldn't be happening."

"You must want something very much," I say.

"That's the problem. Wanting a certain result."

"Does it matter the motivation, once there's the shift?"

"When I listen to LeClair, something

opens. But I don't live there. Fifty years of trying—I should be able to sustain it by now. My three-year-old granddaughter is more present. Time to face *facts*," she says. "My attention is so fragile, so weak, so—"

"Miraculous."

Her head tilts to the side. "Why 'miraculous'?"

"Because it brings us into direct contact with the sacred."

"But it never lasts. Most of the time I'm not even interested. Those are the *facts*." She uses the word like a hammer.

How different, how fearless and willing she was about all this, in her youth (so she tells me). Now at the mere mention at lunch that to get invited back all first-timers must tell a story at meals, Irene panics. Speak in front of everyone? The blunt expression on her face says "No."

Before lunch is over, Tom from New York asks the question for all, "What makes for a good story?"

"A master storyteller is always a master," says LeClair. "His function is to bring one home to oneself."

Irene twists the ring around her finger. What else?

"Don't use 'I.' The best story is indirect—can penetrate deeper." LeClair changes the subject, announcing the topic for the evening discussion.

New wrinkle! It's the very question Irene's father used to ask: "What does it mean to have faith?" It surprises her to hear LeClair say that "beliefs are our biggest addiction" but that "faith is something quite different." She wants to hear more, but lunch is over. All LeClair says is "The stream of Attention is there. Be touched by it, link with it. Not ideas, beliefs, techniques—but *that touch*."

Irene is eager for the evening meeting—until she sees LeClair seated at the back of the hall, part of the audience. The only chair left is quite near his, so she sits there.

The conversation drones on. She can barely hear it. Soon she dozes off—head flops forward—

When she opens her eyes, LeClair is looking at her. He leans in and whispers, "I'm a little disappointed in the discussion. They have not done a very good job." His tone says, *You didn't miss much.*

How kind. Like they are old friends. Why should she feel alone? Is not our sun a part of the universe? Does not a beam go straight from the sun into every beating heart?

Now she *must* get invited back. She must have more time with LeClair; she has questions.

Meal after meal the obligation to tell a story weighs on her. She listens to accounts of travels, spouses, kids, parents, grandparents, pets; the supernatural; fairy tales, confessions, riddles, myths, jokes, parables, fables. After each teller finishes, always the moment of anticipation, awaiting LeClair's response. "That's number 44," he might say, having heard it all before. Sometimes no comment. *The stories people tell always show something about themselves.*

At week's end on a warm day, with a few others Irene hikes the path to town. Tom offers to carry her backpack. Irene chooses to go last in line; she likes it when the others disappear around the bend so it feels like she is alone with the snow-capped peaks. She lets herself fall behind—but the hikers always stop and wait for her. The instant she catches up, they start walking again, so she never gets to rest. Finally, she tells them to go ahead.

Now she can stroll on her own—perfect. Her shoes do not hold her ankles well (the plane lost her boots), but all she cares about is being with the mountains. She comes to a fork in the path. Which way? She didn't think to ask the route. *Foolish woman.*

On the slope just above is a *wandersweg* sign naming the directions. She can't read it at this distance (she rarely wears glasses anymore, such a bother), so she steps up onto some rocks—loose—

Her foot slips—

Down!

The shock. On the ground. Legs splayed. All her weight on her inner right thigh. *How bad?* She slowly brings her legs together. *Try to get up?* Not another person in sight.

Minutes later, coming down the path—

Tom kneels next to her. "Are you okay?" He hands her a bottle of water. "I thought you might need this."

"Thank you, thank you." She sips the

water. She tells him what happened. A truer self appears. "I'm so sorry, going off on my own like that. So arrogant."

"Can you stand?" He helps her up, one arm around her back and under her armpit, to be sure she does not fall.

Standing feels okay. When she takes a step, she can't put her full weight on her right side without discomfort, so Tom gives her his hiking stick to lean on.

With the "cane," she walks unassisted, Tom by her side. She says little, concentrating on the way she places each foot on the ground so there is no pain. Every footfall, filled with attention. In the quiet, all that is personal drops away. The ecstasy of the empty cupboard.

Resting in bed and taking arnica restore her. She is surprisingly better—grateful to walk—and determined to attend the final dinner because it is her last chance to tell a story. One comes to her, a favorite from childhood, about a monkey-like creature, the Tajar, who makes death-defying leaps through the trees, and despite being told not to, dances in the moonlight.

In the dining hall she is ready to tell it—but the instant someone finishes a story, someone else speaks. Irene waits, heart pounding, body like a drum.

A lull. A leap of faith—

"This story impressed me as a child." How loud her voice sounds! The narrative unfolds, complete with hand gestures. *Pretty weird, eh?* Yet the telling itself feels like a joyous leaping from branch to branch.

When she finishes, LeClair asks, "Where is that story from?"

"Africa. I grew up there."

"I think I'll have to hire you to tell stories to my grandchildren." It's just as if he'd said, "Bravo."

After the meal, men and women come up to her in the dining hall to share stories of tricksters like the Tajar. Elbow to elbow with everyone, Irene feels she is "part of a single living organism, we live so close to one another."

We are stargazing on the terrace under a crescent moon.

"I waited too long to come here," she says. "I knew about this place. I had the chance. I regret my own stupidity."

"It's okay right now though, isn't it? The story you told was magical."

"I felt a great risk in telling it."

"But you were yourself."

"I was going to ask LeClair the real point of having us tell stories," says Irene, "but then something happened. I was on my way out of the dining hall, he was speaking to someone else, but he linked his arm with mine, and all three of us walked together. It was like dancing. He wasn't even looking at me—there was this other person he was talking to—but the way he took hold of my arm, it was like he was telling me, through my arm, everything I needed to know. That there is a lovely, light, simple, happy world right here and now. That only the slightest shift is needed to be in it."

In the heavens, a pinpoint of light trembles....

Irene says, "The way he took hold of my arm"—even now to feel the *touch*— "answered all my questions."

STORY 8

Heads Up

*Removing the beam
from Dan's eye.*

High in the Swiss Alps, at the front of a great hall filled with seekers, LeClair asks, "Who here thinks they have a reliable mind?"

The four people most lost in thought raise their hands. That's how Dan sees it. After decades of these summer retreats, he knows what the takeaway will be—You are not what you think—but when will he feel the truth of it?

The task for the four volunteers is to report at dinner everything said now at lunch. The question under discussion: what is the relationship between knowledge, being, and understanding?

Dan has been hauling boulders all morning and, not young, wants to nap. People give their views. Elegant concepts. Articulate theories. Dan wishes he could press the MUTE button.

"The awakened state is...."

All in the head. Full of ideas. The bait is not the fish!

"We're powerless when it comes to..."

You don't know what you're talking about.

"...my nothingness in the face of the great Unknown...."

Even the known is unknown.

One-upping every speaker like this... old thought form... feels wrong. Just listen, he reminds himself. Others experience the world differently. But when will it not be theoretical, divine Love, unconditioned joy—annoying to hear spoken about when one is struggling.

Dan turns away to watch giant puffed-up clouds stream by the window. *A chalet in the clouds—*

"Dan," comes LeClair's voice. "Do you know the saying that begins, 'All men are dead'?"

"Uh... not sure."

"It's from the 12th century Sufi, Dzou'l Noun." LeClair recites slowly—as the volunteers lean in—

"All men are dead except those who know. All those who know are dead except those who practice. All those who practice are dead except those who act with right intention. And those who act with right intention are all in grave danger."

Grave danger. Said with a twinkle in the eye, but Dan feels the accuracy of it. *Lord, help me be aware enough to know I'm not awake.*

At dinner the volunteers report what was said at lunch. No two accounts are alike. The words have fallen differently on the different types.

"So this is a reliable mind," says LeClair.

More questions and discussion. *We're professionals at this.*

LeClair teases, "Your answers give the illusion of being intelligent."

"What's frustrating," Dan speaks up, "is coming into a state in which I understand better what's taking place, and then in the next moment I don't, but act as if I do. What is the right use of the mind?" *You'll go far listening to me.*

"Not to confuse the one who thinks with the one who is aligned," says LeClair. "Instead of my mind-dominated usual condition, my wavering state, with an active attention something refined can penetrate. When very quiet inside—need an atmosphere of sensitivity—aware of breathing—this other Attention appears, deep Intelligence. If the mind starts to think about this or that, not necessary now, let it go. I don't want to lose contact with this Intelligence because it's precious, so I return, not to grasp at it—not imagination and thought—but a very active attention."

The sparkliness in the room doubles.

He adds, "Thinking breaks the charm."

It's the first time Dan hears the word *intelligence* with what sounds like a capital I. An Intelligence that bypasses thought? Clearly, it's not the voice-in-the-head that says, "I get it and you don't." *Lord, help me to be conscious.*

Later Dan is put in charge of the entertainment for the final night's celebration. A T.V. sitcom veteran, he often helps LeClair in this way. There is such a warm feeling between them because with Dan there is no pretense and always a funny comment. But what to do this week that hasn't been done before?

Inspiration comes at dinner as people tell stories, a rite of passage for newbies if they want to get invited back. Some of the tales are quirky. A Native American gentleman brags about his tribe's "extraordinary ability always to know which direction we're facing." LeClair blindfolds him, spins him around, and asks which direction, but the man can't get it right. Dan knows the feeling. Where's the compass? Where true north?

Dessert is served—but the ice cream sits melting in the bowls while everyone is forced to listen to "Woody, the Remarkable Dog." Woody's owner, the misguided teller of All Tales Woody, never once refers to Woody with a pronoun but repeats the name—for the hundredth Woody time!

When it's over, LeClair comments, "You are never to do that again."

Everyone eats dessert. The woman next to Dan is annoyed. "Sorry you had to listen to my husband go on and on about losing his dog. All day long for years he was all sweetness with that dog—'Oh, puppy, puppy.' But when he talks to me, it's always, 'What? Are you nuts?'" She sighs. "I guess I'm just glad something made him that cheery for that long." She points to the dessert bowl. "Can you tell what it was?"

Dan assesses the swirly liquid and chunks. "Chocolate soup?"

"It was ice cream with pears and chocolate sauce. We served 90 portions at the last possible minute to keep it cold, and everyone was about to taste it when we were forced to listen to that dog story. Next time I'll bake a cake."

"Yes, all the sad tales," says Dan. "I didn't realize I was so happy."

"Got any aspirin?"

"Maybe we should put it on the cake."

People and their stories. *Could be funny,* the 1001 things we get identified with, so noticeable in others. Play it for laughs?

By week's end Dan and friends have prepared skits in hats, culminating in a rambling monologue of the week's peak bits. Mount D'Analogue. His arms hidden, Dan philosophizes as Professor Snellby ("Let me tell you about the Unknown") while a friend unseen behind him "does" Dan's arms making funny hand gestures. The performance, a hit. *It's great to see LeClair laugh.*

The next morning, at the last meal before people return home, Dan sits cross-legged on a cushion in the first row facing LeClair who is saying, "How to develop sustained attention? Be passionate about it. 'Passionating' in it. Being awake in this finer energy is like being in the shower. 'In it' feels completely different. Bathe in it, with all of you."

Dan smiles. For a moment it's like lying on the beach in the sun and everything is okay. No need to control things. No concern for the future; there is no next moment. The sole urgency now: in every second attending to this Light.

Dan takes a bite of his scrambled eggs when—suddenly—of all things—

He gets up. He goes to his dorm. When he returns to the dining hall, he encounters a silence so deep that his feet scurfing along the floor make the only sound. He is about to sit down when LeClair looks up at him.

Dan waits a beat, then says, "I forgot my

teeth."

The room erupts with laughter. Yes, it is funny. And he plays it for laughs. But right away he feels bad. *A smartass comment at the wrong moment.* Back in his place, he looks down at his eggs, cold on the plate.

All morning he thinks: a sacred moment, the culmination of the week's work, and *I stepped on it.* He locates LeClair supervising the dismantling of the large tent that was the men's dorm.

"I'm sorry about breakfast," says Dan. "I ruined the moment. All together in that wonderful silence."

"No, no. You got me off the hook."

"How hard it is to use the head in the right way. It's not so much what happens that makes me unhappy, it's what the voice in my head says about it. Believing it. Until now."

"The attention is not yet pure to be completely aligned with this energy— no thoughts—needs the silence. Other vibrations are there perhaps, yet just to be attracted, so at moments... to be one with this pure Attention." As LeClair walks off, he says, "Come for tea later and we'll talk."

Nearby six men shoulder a heavy pallet that was the tent floor and carry it up the incline. Dan moves quickly toward them to help. Just as he reaches them, they stop short—

He walks right into the metal edge. Whack!

He's down on the ground. Blood trickles from a gash on his forehead. Two doctors come quickly. The eye is okay—lucky. They clean the wound. But how to close it? Stitch it?

LeClair arrives, examines the cut, and puts a Band-Aid on it. He says, *so funny and sweet*, "This is not the way to use your head."

The two men sit together on the hillside.

Dan feels like the Zen meditator newly conked on the noggin by the "head" monk to wake up.

LeClair says, "Are you okay?"

Dan only nods; thoughts knocked right out of him. He's watching two women hang pillowcases on the clothesline. Bend, step, reach; bend, step, reach; a dance. The meadow in sunlight; the women moving among the flowers, the atmosphere around them, around him—what bliss.

"So… it's not about figuring out anything," Dan says finally, "when I'm lucky enough to direct connectly." *Direct connectly?* He chuckles. "I can't think and I can't speak."

"Why don't you start a group when you get home," LeClair surprises him. "Maybe you know someone who's interested."

"I'm no teacher." Dan has looked beneath the golden robes of the spiritually well-endowed. *Grave danger.* "My ego would get too involved. It thinks it's a competition."

"There is a need for something to pass, to circulate. The Light, moving always through everything. No ideas about it."

"But people want to talk about ideas. I used to. Can't stuff that turkey anymore."

"When the fish is caught, throw away the net."

"Good to hear," says Dan. "When I'm like this—very focused—I understand what you say. But the fish is slippery. I can talk as if I'm serving Something that I'm not actually aware of anymore." He stops. It occurs to him, "Is that what the head is for? To monitor that, so there's a coming back?"

"The calling back of the attention has awakening power," says LeClair. "Going away and coming back are part of the same oneness, the same process. If taken, it means I'm concentrated on me, my functions, a thought, a feeling, a reaction. So remember this other mode of being, more sensitive, just receiving." He pauses. "When you are dispersed, let the Attention touch your state. Just be sure you're really letting the contact appear. See the power in you." We have greater capacity than we know!

A movement from above makes Dan look up. Blackbirds swooping in the high currents. Tree limbs swaying, each in its own tempo, yet all of one motion. The wavering compass steadies, oriented to a new possibility.

"It's like the mind has stepped aside," says Dan. "I hear you, but right now none of it starts up thoughts. Or if something tries to start, not getting stuck to it. This other quality that's here... needs everything, every bit of attention in every second, to recognize it, stay joined with it. That is how it feels."

"It is the state of not being taken. When

the energy comes through, it is a taste of freedom—no mind—and when you are connected with that, you don't have to pretend."

"And what about always wanting to point out where someone else is going wrong?"

LeClair turns to him. "That is because you still think it's yours, this experience. Like a little bit of carpet that needs to have a speck taken off. You think it belongs to you. There is no *you*. It is complete identification. Either one is identified with the body or one is in this flow, the true Self."

The Most Natural Thing in the World

Can Murphy begin a new chapter?

So the trick is to find the right moment to bring LeClair his coffee still hot. If there are voices from inside his room, someone is meeting with him and best not to interrupt. That's what Murphy is told in the kitchen at the retreat, now that he's assigned to bring LeClair his mid-morning tray, an honor usually reserved for one of the Geneva group often here at the chalet. It's "American" week, Murphy's first time in Switzerland, and he wants to make a good impression, but he's nervous he'll mess up—unacceptable!

"What does he like for a snack?" Murphy asks in the kitchen, knowing LeClair probably has peculiar (European) tastes.

"Maybe a little bread. With some pâté. From the tube in the pantry drawer. Maybe a pickle."

To deliver the tray, Murphy dresses up in a clean shirt (his idea of formal is no stains) and places in his pocket a small spiral notebook. You know the story. Wannabe writer moves to New York City and goes through a series of disappointments. A pity, too, because he ruled at college—editor of this, winner of that; they contemplated naming a dorm after him. But time has stolen his collegiate remarkableness. Will his sojourn on the mountain serve up something worth writing?

After three mornings bringing the same snack, Murphy hears LeClair announce to the ninety people at breakfast, "And whoever is bringing my tray, no more pickles!" It is said amicably—something about talking to people without pickle breath—but of course LeClair knows who brings it. Such a simple thing: why didn't Murphy notice, when clearing, always the pickle left on the plate? *Idiot!*

The following morning, thankfully, no tray to fix. At 4 a.m. Murphy zips up his fleece hoodie and puts his notebook in his pocket. A rare event: half the "camp" go off-property to hike to the top of the Weisshorn.

Sunrise at the peak. Seated on the rocky heights, Murphy composes a poem. The clear geometry of a lake. A gust, serrying the water's surface, now blue, now the color of gunmetal.

When the hikers return, over lunch they gush about the experience, to which LeClair says, "Being with the greatness of Nature, another quality appears, another self, connected to something outside time and space. The joy you feel—not for you but to connect you, as in prayer."

But some who didn't go complain. Tom grumbles, "I'm sorry, but what I see is that I'm dead asleep most of the time. Maybe not on a mountaintop. But the rest of the time I'm really a slave to my thoughts, continually, one after another."

Me, too. More voices commiserate. "I see that I can't…." "I see that I don't…." "I see than I couldn't…."

"*Seeing* is a blessing," says LeClair. "It is never negative. It is objective. It comes from Above. Seeing allows this higher energy to appear so I can be related to it. Beating myself up is something else." LeClair looks directly at Tom and says with great kindness, "Where is the Love?"

The room becomes still. A tenderness in the air. *Put down the whip.*

"It is good to feel dissatisfaction that I don't correspond to this finer energy," says LeClair. "That comes from an intelligence. At the moment I see my inadequacy, something can open. This incompleteness calls me."

Murphy is concerned that, hearing all the complaining, LeClair will think the hike was a bad idea—

Give him the poem, so at least he knows the trip was worthwhile.

In the morning Murphy carries the tray down the steps, careful to keep the coffee level. Will there ever be a moment he isn't nervous at LeClair's door? "*Être, pas paraître,*" LeClair once said in passing, and Murphy knows what the French sound-alikes mean: *To be, not to pretend.*

The door is ajar. No one there. Great. Murphy puts down the tray and places on it the poem.

All day he waits but not a glance. *Has*

LeClair read it? Does he know who wrote it? Can he understand it if it's not in French? Click-click-click.

The next morning, on the tray, another poem, this one in French. Murphy knocks, hoping to leave it in secret—

"Come in." LeClair looks up from the yellow pad covered with spidery writing. He indicates the chair opposite him. Murphy sits. Their first one-on-one. His neck is stiffer than a stale biscuit.

LeClair asks about Murphy's life back in the States.

Murphy does not feel safe enough to say why he's really crossed an ocean (disillusioned with longtime spiritual teacher— ugly split—*now what?*). Instead he offers quotidian details of matters that don't matter, all the while thinking *I'm not telling the truth.* And yet, regardless of that thought or the words coming out of his mouth, it's okay. *Let it be. Come back.*

Different!

A sudden non sequitur: "I think you must be a very good editor," says LeClair.

What? How does he…?

LeClair searches through papers on his desk and brings forth galleys of an article. "Make corrections?"

Really? Instantly Murphy worries about marking in ink the only copy. "I don't have a pencil with an eraser."

LeClair begins an exhaustive search of the room. The desk, the bed table, even the bed covers. The longer he fumbles, the more pathetic he looks to Murphy who says, "Oh, please, no, it's not important," *you poor, dear, old man.*

A stub of a pencil is found. Murphy takes it and leaves.

First page, second, third. Murphy has studied every sort of spiritual book but never read anything that speaks to him like these pages. The English is perfect, too, not a single correction needed, so why? Quickly Murphy copies out the text, permission or not, because he'll have to give back the galleys and will want to read the words again.

When he returns the galleys, nothing is said about the poems. Later, though—did Murphy hear right? In a small-group meeting LeClair uses a certain phrase, and isn't

it the very one from the Weisshorn poem?
Is this his way of acknowledging it without
revving up the ego? Click-click-click.

At lunch LeClair calls for volunteers to
translate a text into English so it can be read
to everyone. "Who knows French?"

A few hands go up. Murphy would never
put himself forward for such an important task, but during rest period, someone
fetches him from his bed. "LeClair wants
you to work on this."

The translation team consists of three
Americans and an older French woman.
Murphy joins them on the terrace. They all
go—surprise!—into LeClair's room.

LeClair hands out copies of the spidery
writing.

Murphy sits on the floor with the others,
leaning back against the bed, knees up, notepad and pen in hand.

The team translates the French into
English: *"There exists inside you an energy of
extraordinary intensity. You can perceive its
life. You don't have to—"*

Someone offers American slang for a
French phrase.

LeClair smiles. "What's this you say, 'cry crocodile tears'?"

People chuckle. Even more slang is offered a few sentences later, to which LeClair asks, "What means this 'scatterbrained'?" And, "What is 'chatterbox'?"

They're all laughing so hard, Murphy can hardly believe *this* is the oh-so-serious work of the translation team. How great it feels—the most natural thing in the world—to be present like this with LeClair. That wonderful laugh of his; how easily he lets it loose, like a pet off a leash.

At the end of the session, LeClair says that the team "might work again, if time" before dinner, but now he has to go to a meeting "for new people."

Murphy stays behind. "Can I come? I'm new." He grins. How free he feels. Yesterday he could never have said that.

At the meeting, Murphy is galvanized by LeClair's voice: "Now that there is contact with this finer energy, a conviction of it, a living in it—must let go of all the old ideas. Give all the attention to receiving this energy."

If only Murphy could embed in himself

what he's hearing, for it carries the quality of attention being lived now, and surely he will need the words when he's on his own. It occurs to him to "record" a key phrase on a fingertip to hold a few sentences, allowing him to continue to listen fully.

Another phrase, another fingertip. "We are all the same, have this energy, this Intelligence. There is no difference. And when this central Intelligence appears, to respect it. If only you knew what it is, could see what it is, you would know its worth. Not for self-glory. Not for a nice experience and then you are passive again. But as a truth felt in oneself."

When the room becomes silent, Murphy reviews the first three phrases. Still there. Then the first six. After the hour, all ten fingers have a few words set in each.

Murphy comes out of the meeting walking quickly, intent on not stopping for anyone. Sitting on his bed, he lists the ten phrases, then fills in whole sentences as they reappear intact. No paraphrasing. Because the words are not conceptual. They are vibrational. They carry something higher and must be set down exactly.

The dinner bell. Keep writing.

The dining hall is full when Murphy finally sits down beside one of the "new" people. "Am I late?"

"We've eaten."

The joke feels perfect. "You look happy."

"Such an amazing meeting."

"Yes," says Murphy. "At first when I came in, I could care less about any of you. At the end, I would have given you a kidney."

The two men look like laughing buddhas. Not the smelly *we-know-better-than-every-one-else-heh-heh* kind of laugh but the *ain't-it-good-to-be-alive* kind.

Servers hand along plates of food.

LeClair walks in. He stops in front of Murphy, who looks up at him.

"We waited for you," says LeClair. "We had work."

Murphy nods. LeClair walks on.

Missed it. The translation meeting. Completely forgot.

Scolded by LeClair!

Yet… how strange. There's no sting in it. No click-click-click about it.

Murphy says matter-of-factly, "I always

mess up." The expanded state remains. Where is the one who worries each time what LeClair thinks of him?

That night, in LeClair's room, Murphy and the team finish the translation at 2 a.m. They say goodnight and step outside. Cold air, clear sky. Murphy looks up. Amid a trillion galaxies of a hundred billion stars, something is different now.

Early Saturday morning he types the translation. When he comes to the final paragraph, the words strike him for the first time. "*You know the way,*" it says. "*You can ascend the path much farther now relying on yourself,*" it says. "*But the wish must be there, and the effort must be there. He is helped who helps himself.*"

Instantly joy rises up at the thought, true or not, that the message is meant for him. Is it not the answer to the very question he never asked, about finding another teacher? Presence, the teacher now. And the message is clear: You *can* wake up. You *can* rely on yourself. Not only that. *You must.*

Thrilling! An old narrative drops away, the one about awakening as a problem, a goal for some future self—not at all what it feels like now, like this, alive in this way.

Listen… to life in this moment….

Even at LeClair's door Murphy is at ease—how is that possible—handing over the typescript and saying what an honor it was to work on it.

LeClair bypasses this bit of exuberant humility, and with an unforgettably encouraging smile—as if they've just finished a long conversation—says, "I know you can do it."

On departure day, translation done and poems forgotten, Murphy goes to collect the morning tray.

LeClair leaves his desk and walks with Murphy up the incline toward the kitchen.

Midway, they stop.

LeClair says, "The poems. You wrote?"

"Yes."

LeClair goes on his way.

Sunlight transfigures the trees. The fluttering wing. And nothing else in the world but gladness filling the heart… there is no telling….

I turned from the pines with an idiot smile on my face.

Another Kind of Love

What counts for Paulina.

On a porch in the Alps, Paulina slices bread. She delivers the platter to the kitchen where Saturday lunch preparations are underway. It's the last full day of the last retreat of the season. The week has been challenging. The thought of no more summers working with LeClair is disorienting, lunar in its pull. *The party is over when the guest of honor leaves.*

There's time before lunch to walk in the woods. *Stay in concentration, not go far away from myself.* An earthy scent. Moss greening the rocks. Pines rising to the sky. The path is uneven—must mind the roots arching up from the ground. And then, the clearing. Where sunshine falls unobstructed. Where a year ago Paulina stood with her husband. She feels his absence as near to her as the summer air.

A buck charges by! A lone doe stops, raises her head, bounds into the woods. Paulina has stood here before, found deer here before, yet only today does she see the imprints their bodies made in the matted ferns.

"See?" Paulina calls out her husband's name. "Happy anniversary."

"Happy anniversary," she hears him say in her mind.

"Our first interdimensional anniversary."

"That's exactly how to think about it," he says.

But she's remembering the hospital, the final days, his "Let me go—"

"Don't go there," he says. "I'm here."

"How is it for you, where you are?"

"It's great." He reminds her, "No pain."

"I'm so glad for that!" But could she have done more?

"You did great," he says.

Tears well up, come with the contact. She apologizes for them.

"Think about it," he says. "I'm the ideal husband for you now. Never annoyed and never annoying."

Hah! Why tell yourself he's gone? Think different!

Back in the dorm she gathers up her clothing designs; she wants to become a master pattern maker but that takes time. She packs them in her carry-on. Ticking off things to do. Delay departure? Depends on how LeClair is feeling—and he's been up half the night making arrangements for others. *Not necessary to think about that now.*

Called to LeClair's room, she walks in to find a 6′ x 6′ opening in the ceiling. A ladder leans against it.

"Go up there for me?" says LeClair. "See what's in the boxes."

A line of people wait outside his door. *So why spend time with me?* Even as she crouches in order to move around the crawl space, she knows to inhabit her body with attention because with LeClair it can never be just about "boxes."

She opens a large container: soft things. Another: hundreds of photos of past retreats. A photo-portrait of LeClair's wife, who has passed. A group shot of forty men with LeClair seated in the outdoor amphitheater. All taken by a talented photographer, her husband. She half expects him to come up the ladder to help carry down boxes.

"You want photos? Take," says LeClair.

The next morning when she brings LeClair his espresso, she sees on his desk an open pack of cigarettes. She wants to scold him. Instead she reports, "It's relaxed in the kitchen, with just the men making the breakfast."

"Now this is information I want to hear," he says.

That smile. How can she help but love what is there in his eyes and wish to correspond to That? Can she free herself from all her concerns and enter the Mystery?

The courtyard fills with luggage. A line forms in the hall where Paulina takes payment for the week. She checks off names and puts the money into an envelope. In their traveling clothes, people look different, yet she sees in each one what shines there.

The special "American breakfast" of bacon and eggs is served outside on the stone walkway that LeClair calls Main Street. He says to her, "Isn't it marvelous, the Street like this?' Today, we are social."

Tom from New York asks LeClair, for all to hear, "What is the change from how we were when we arrived?"

LeClair teases, "There's a pile of feathers on the hill, and the wind will blow them away." He adds, "It is so striking when people are very quiet, turned toward what calls them 'innerly' and not at all taken by whatever is around them. Each face becomes beautiful."

"I feel… transparent," says someone.

"There's only one thing to do when you're feeling transparent," says LeClair. "The sun at high noon. No shadows."

"Will you come to the U.S. to see us this fall?"

"If I can," says LeClair, "but if I cannot, everything will be all right, either way."

If I cannot?

"How can we keep this connection when we leave?"

LeClair turns to Paulina to speak.

"Even when we leave here and maybe forget," says Paulina, "we have been imprinted with something precious. We can recall it. We can touch another kind of love that is not our self-love. Of the universe, of another level. And it is that which is important. You and me, together, for that."

The whole world, poised for a moment. Companions together in pure attention.

No one speaks. LeClair says playfully, "All your questions are answered."

People smile.

He finishes the sentence, "...by being in the Now. It is a great gift, to join with something very natural in our deepest nature. We can then forgive all misunderstanding between human beings. When the attention is with this other energy permeating me— very concentrated yet very light, free, wishing nothing, needing nothing—everything is put into order naturally. Everything opens to this—the head, the heart. Everything can be there in this. And this energy is still not the highest...."

Breakfast over. Hugs, handshakes. Bags disappear from the courtyard. Paulina puts the kitchen in order. Laurence mops the floor. Seymour scrubs the walls; he and Jason will stay late to finish. In the women's dorm, Alice empties the trash. Mary and

Angie hang a hundred little pillowcases on the clothesline. Murphy sits with his notebook open to the sky; a butterfly lands on the page. Irene puts away the gardening tools. Nicholas asks Tom, "Is there room in your car for one more?" Vehicles come and go. Gratitude and responsibility. Objectivity and steady observation. A man can travel inward where he is, knowing that all life is the manifestation of a single Mystery.

Soon Paulina will have to leave, unsure when she will see LeClair again. She must ask him what more needs doing.

A doctor comes out of LeClair's room. "Give him a moment."

Oh, God. How quickly she hacks a disaster out of whole cloth.

She knocks.

"Come in." LeClair is propped up on the bed.

"I found this." She hands him a photo of his wife; he looks glad to have it. "So, all the photos," says Paulina. "I need to know what to do with them."

"When the time comes, you'll know what to do." He gets up. "Follow me." He leads her to a small room with a folding table and two chairs. He begins emptying onto the table several large manila envelopes. A flurry of paper bills and the clink of coins. It's the money collected all summer to cover expenses.

"We'll count it," he says.

She expects he will leave her alone to do the sorting, but he stays. His gaze steadies her in wakefulness. He shows her how to wrap the coins. She is surprised that this is what he wants to do, but then not surprised, because for him there are no unimportant activities. They work together in silence. What arises in her—it's the love of *being*, and the love that comes with *being*. For in that very room for that hour, consciousness blazes up. High noon.

When they finish counting, LeClair says, "This has been a very creative experience."

Only he would put it that way. *Yes, it's very different, isn't it, when the energy comes.*

"Wait here," he tells her. "I have something for you." When he returns, he carries a white cotton blouse that is exquisitely designed. Paulina recognizes it as his wife's.

The gift makes Paulina feel deeply cared for, so much so that for years to come, whenever she sees it, she is reminded that *perhaps one day I might care as much for my soul as he does.*

Later, bags in the car, her plane leaving soon, Paulina goes to LeClair's room to say goodbye. The oxygen tank is pulled out from under the desk. Heart drops. "I'll miss you."

"You don't have to miss anything." He lifts both arms wide to the sides, as if to embrace the whole world. "It's all around!"

At the door he takes her hand, bows to kiss it. They are eye to eye. He says, "We have good work together."

It's what he wishes us all to feel: we help each other by living in this pure attention.

In the car, all the way down the mountain, the scent of his cologne on her hand. Affection for him catches in her throat and hollows her chest with the pain of separation.

The highway along Lake Geneva. The waters, Pacific blue.

Paulina calls out to her husband, "Are you here?"

"I'm right here."

"I'm so glad," she says.

"All is well."

"It helps so much to hear that."

"We are one."

She says, "In our light-bodies?"

"We are Light buddies."

Hah! Not gone. Not lost.

Then she hears, "We have good work together."

All at once the possibility occurs to her: LeClair... Not lost either? Beyond forms, thoughts, space, time... tomorrow, next month, twenty years from now.... *We have good work together!*

Sunlight flashes on the lake.

Whatever comes and goes, I AM.

Light cells in motion, sparks of a larger ocean....

Let everything drop away. Recognize this unknown force appearing.

Receive it. Join it.

Creates love in you, consciousness in you.

And through you, in the world.

At the airport, Paulina parks the car and sits quietly for a moment. Vehicles hurry by. Yet there is calm. There is stillness, potent, shining.

With full care, she opens the door.

The light of the world streams in, warm and beckoning.

CODA

Notes from a Meeting

Higher consciousness at 7000 feet.

A great joy breaks free of the self
And joins the moving river of presence.

—Rumi

July, Switzerland

Everything we need is here in us. Everything for fuller being. There is a kind of sacred descent of attention that can bring this about. Seeing the obstacles, thoughts, feelings, yes, perhaps a pressure that keeps me from it. But if I can relax inside, just allow the pure attention to flow in, be in that. Very natural. It's what we are.

Attention: a sacred energy coming into me. Be sensitive to it. Recognize again and again that it is there.

For many years we try methods, but then, at moments, there is enough energy for a sensitivity to appear, and then for this Intelligence to appear. It is not the methods that produce it. It's letting everything be, inside, just as it is, and opening to the attention.

Completely relaxed....

Something fine can fill me.

There is joy in recognizing this action within.

Freedom in a moment, freedom from fear and being anxious, free to be just as I am, giving all to what is number one in me.

Perhaps it takes thirty minutes, perhaps five minutes, sometimes, perhaps five seconds. The whole of me becomes sensitive to this Intelligence, this central attention, listening for it. We were made for it.

Then I'm not thinking about me but can listen, aware of breathing, called to stand in the place that can receive impressions.

Sensitivity everywhere. Nothing but sensitivity....

A kind of whole-hearted emptiness. A trusting emptiness.

So that a finer influence can act on me, in the silence.

And even despite myself, I begin to receive it, yield to it, a channel for it.

And perhaps a threshold is reached when I belong to That.

~

Made in the USA
Monee, IL
30 June 2022

98885129R00098